John P. Shea

# THE SEX LIFE OF THE UNMARRIED ADULT

# THE SEX LIFE OF THE UNMARRIED ADULT

## AN INQUIRY INTO AND AN INTERPRETATION OF CURRENT SEX PRACTICES

EDITED BY IRA S. WILE, M.D.



GARDEN CITY PUBLISHING CO., INC., NEW YORK

1940
GARDEN CITY PUBLISHING CO., INC.



CL

MANUFACTURED IN THE UNITED STATES OF AMERICA

DEDICATED

to those who seek truth,

unafraid of tradition,

undeterred by taboo

"The concealment of truth
is the only indecorum known to science."

WESTERMARCK

# PREFACE

EVERY NEW civilization is the result of a change of mental clothes. Every new civilization theoretically is an improvement on an earlier state of barbarism. The term, "barbarism," is applied to any pattern of life regarded as rude, savage, contrary to the accepted type of behavior, and, above all, inferior because foreign to the thinking of those who sit in judgment upon its nature, influences and ideals. When one civilization supplants another the gods of the vanquished become new devils for the victors.

Civilization does not represent a static state, although each age and nation regards its achievements as possessing the highest survival values for mankind. By its very nature, the civilizing process is dynamic and involves change. Our present era has resulted from numerous modifications of the arts of life. Science allegedly has increased our enlightenment and refinement but our natures are not machines nor machine-made.

Buckle noted that only those conscious of darkness seek light. Man alters his mode of life as he refuses to remain a slave to traditions outworn and to ideas no longer tenable. Successive generations of man may pass retaining the belief of their unparalleled accomplishment and be condemned by succeeding generations for incompetence, degeneration or failure. To the Greeks all others were Barbarians. To those of the twentieth century, the nineteenth appears dull, unproductive and ineffective. Queen Victoria reigned many decades but her moral contributions do not prevail in this Prince of Wales era.

Each age finds the necessity for greater illumination, struggles to advance in terms of current civilizing forces and then is obliged to pass from the scene because of the direct opposition of royalist, cleric or revolutionary mob. One cannot civilize men merely by urging their whole-souled acceptance of the dictates of the past. That which was deemed good by their fathers may not suit their tastes or meet their needs. Continuous education of the masses may raise the per capita knowledge and power of the group but it fails to advance the line of the leaders. Leaders must lead and this is impossible if they are shackled to conformity with past ideas.

Past generations have released man from various threatening forces inherent in Nature without any essential alteration of his own nature. He has striven to control his world of earth, air and water. He has studied the infinitely small even to the structure of the atom; he has reached out into the universe and opened an exposition with light from the distant star Arcturus. He has harnessed the water and the winds; he has solidified gases and volatilized metals; he has dared and died to conquer man's enemies and to explore the heights, the depths and the lengths of his world. The strife for the conquest of his own soul has been less consistent.

His own organizations, or societies, have been manipulated in terms of ambitious competitions for power by specific groups—national, racial, guild, familial and individual. The rights of all men too frequently have been sacrificed in the interest of the privileges of the few. The doctrine of individualism developed and flourished. To be free became the aim of all men. As a result social strength increased through the granting of freer personal activity in the struggle for existence and accumulation.

Recently another tentative theory has developed which denies the validity of the traditional individualism and accepts the general principle that the good of all people can and should be founded upon a greater and more unselfish group cohesion. Whether one thinks of Russia, Italy, Germany or the New Deal in America, there is ample and widening recognition that the individual and the state have reciprocal relationships. It is the familiar "all for one and one for all" slogan for mutual protection and welfare.

Our present civilization is, therefore, subjected to new strains and pressures—economic, moral and religious. The lives of men and women of diverse age groups are definitely affected, not merely in terms of their gross obligations to the state, but in terms of the emergence of individual life in harmony with new doctrines and untested philosophies. It is natural, therefore, to observe marked changes in sexual thinking and conduct among the married—and even more among the unmarried. The old pleas for freedom and individualism have found expression in freer sex behaviors and more open sex relations between unmarried men and women.

Every modification of economic status, and every transformation of social program alters national philosophies directly. The evolutionary phases of public opinion, sentiment and judgment are consequential outgrowths of the shifting emphases of persistent minorities. Pioneering groups lead social thought and practice along strange pathways. Eventually they overcome opposition and their activities are less harshly criticized. Gradually they are imitated until finally they are identified with the normal life experience of a citizenry with limited initiative. Human nature resists its own artificial suppression, argues against it and becomes emboldened to experiment in new modes of escape from its own denial.

The essential forces in the universe may still be reduced to rather simple terms—hunger and love, the need for sustenance and the urge to perpetuation. Hunger has been viewed primarily as an economic factor. Man's basic appetite for food (and one may add clothing and shelter, as they affect dietetics quantitatively and qualitatively), has constituted the foundation of the struggle for existence. The organization of tribes during nomadism through the period of hunting and agriculture, and the politico-economic evolution in the fixed habitations, down to the modern economic industrial system, has been vitally concerned with hunger.

The sexual urge, which ever has been under social regulation, has been viewed in partial relationship to economics and available food supplies. It has been given special recognition in the form of regulative and restrictive forces because sexual life usually has been appropriated, if not exalted, as a function to be utilized in the interest of the State. The birth rate and the food supplies of migrating peoples were of economic-social significance. The urge to controlled propagation and the correction of over-propagation, through infanticide, abortion and contraception, have been noted throughout man's history. One may think of aborting Melanesians, infanticidal Hyperboreans and Chinese, and the Spartans with selective exposure of infants, but there are also the demands of Il Duce for greater birth release and the subsidies for productive marriage under the present Teutonic régime. Famine, war and industrialism invoke social concern with fecundity and sexual relations.

The sexual urge in terms of personal growth and development has not been the primary concern of society. Nonetheless, while there has been a greater consolidation of economic forces during the past hundred years, there has been a greater liberation of sexual forces. With the larger amount of economic centralization and the diminished opportunity for individual direction of economic advancement, more thought has been devoted to personal freedom. From this has grown a sharper challenge to the nature and meaning of the sexual drives. And thus arose definite attempts to interpret sexual life in terms of personality and individual growth.

A new age and gencration evidence the markedly transformed ideas which have been freely circulated and have found considerable personal responsiveness. The development of a freer press, the extension of literary productions in the form of magazines and books and the prompt release of information along scientific lines, with the higher standards of education throughout this country have been accompanied by noteworthy changes in opinions and sentiments. These are manifest in the moot judgments upon the laws of marriage and divorce, as well as in the warring ideas bound up in open discussion of companionate marriage, celibacy, chastity, contraception, sterilization, sex education, the regulation of prostitution and the prophylaxis of venereal diseases. Social hygiene has superseded the limited concept of sex hygiene. Sex is seen not merely as founding and continuing society but as giving it a dynamic value.

The recent influx of psychological theories stressing sex impulses has brought into the open a few facts and many hypotheses concerning the essential nature of man. These provoke vigorous discussion, which induce liberal, even though occasionally bizarre, thinking concerning the primitive and feral nature of the forces motivating man's general behaviors. Freud still is anathema to many who cannot desexualize their critical faculties, just as he is at least a demigod to those whose psyches are merely erogenous zones.

The stage portrays various accepted and rejected forms of sex behavior and raises many quaint and queer questions for many who were unaware of sexual pathology. Motion pictures, with sound, give visual and aural expression to the overt accompaniments of sex play in a manner that offers vicarious experience to the adolescent and the frustrated groups in our population. They stimulate plastic minds to receive new impressions among which long-drawn-out osculation is the simplest and the mildest. In consequence, conscious and unconscious urges have been exercised and exorcised.

In many ways we have had a renascence of primitive worship. Phallicism has not been avowed in the simple manner of the ancients but the sex factor in our civilization has received a tremendous amount of attention. Dancers and preachers, biologists and psychologists, sociologists and moralists have emphasized viewpoints that reveal their deep interest in man's basic nature. A solicitous, though frank, sophistication, occasionally an apologetic intellectual curiosity, shares the spirit of the higher criticism in attacking the epidemic and sporadic inquiries about taboos, regulations, ideas and ideals involved in the sexual nature of man. There is now less stress upon original sin but more upon the original sinner.

A new generation has arisen, fewer in number and becoming still less numerous because of the declining birth rate. Our population is tending to become stabilized. The per capita absorption of formal knowledge is greater than heretofore and the exposure to the informal facts and fancies of life has never been more general. It is natural, therefore, that many changes should arise in connection with our thinking concerning sex, love and marriage. What has been the effect of the economic, social and educational changes of the past generations? Have men changed? Have social ideals altered? Is man more intelligent or more reasonable; has he a higher degree of volitional control over his activities; has his status as a reasoning biped separated him widely from the more instinctive behaviors of his anthropoid ancestors? Has man, during his five hundred thousand years, succeeded in affecting his internal environment sufficiently to alter the instinctive drives common to all animal creation? Is he more or less sex conscious than other animals? Are his emotional relations to himself less subject to the unconscious forces that energize his maturation and creative trends? Data concerning such questions are not wholly available but such challenging queries should not be ignored.

Society emphasizes man's duty to propagate. Hence the sexual morality of the world has been pyramided upon the foundation of marriage. The married represent the conservators of the State, even though they may not always respond to the demand for more workers, more soldiers and more followers. Today the married elders devote considerable time to discussion of the activities of the growing generation who have absorbed in part the changing sexual philosophy of their parents. The so-called wildness of youth and the open revolt of the unmarried are in sharp contrast to the continued smugness and the complacency of the clandestine and hypocritical shifts in the behaviors of many married adults.

Modern sexual problems were not born of today; nor should they all be attributed to the industrial revolution. Modern sexual trends, which deviate from traditional standards of morals and forsake procedures of compulsion founded upon religious sanctions, developed mainly as a function of disillusionment, though not of despair. They are outgrowths of a sense of ineffectual development and inadequacy, incidental to a decline of definite spiritual goals and a diminished sense of security in the permanence of current life purposes. In the United States one finds a very direct reaction to continued reactionary pressures. A sharp swing toward liberated activity has partially offset Comstockian efforts at suppression. Egocentric values are now stressed by reason of an awakening to the meaning of personality and its relationship to fullness of living. It is patent that the sexual problems of the married have materially changed because their outlook upon life and marital relationships has been transformed under the influence of assertive science, selfish materialism, relaxing prosperity and a prevailing concept of ethical relativity.

The married people of the United States constitute the majority of those above the age of fifteen years; but approximately one-third of the people in the United States above the age of fifteen years are unmarried. The nature of the problems and the adjustments of so large a portion of the community cannot be ignored. Married life with its sexual gratifications and satisfactions is conditioned largely by sexual ideas and experiences antedating matrimony. The line of distinction between unmarriage and marriage is a civil rite. The civil rite, however, has little effect upon human physiology, despite its serious influence by reason of the pressure of morals, ethics and social ideals.

The sex life of our unmarried adults merits consideration. The unmarried as well as the married are caught up in the movement of the world, both as individuals and as members of the social group. Their altered views are not purposed; they are not in revolt as individuals; they are exhibiting the sexual reactions symptomatic of their age. Their primal instincts are less inhibited by the current mores but still are subject to their efforts at control in terms of factors inherent in their psycho-biologic organization and in their own socio-economic pressures and religious-ethical ideals.

Numerous volumes have dealt with sex in its various forms, whether generically as sex hygiene, sex education, biology, literary erotica, or as propaganda for definite social theories in relation to prostitution, concubinage, companionate marriage and celibacy. Authors with diverse backgrounds and insight have sought to interpret anthropology, psychology, religion, social organization and the growth of law in the light of their concepts, beliefs and hypotheses concerning the meaning of sexual activity as represented in personal and group rites and ceremonials. Their emphasis generally has been placed upon the implicit factors concerned with the sexual drive itself. Some have sought to reveal hidden meanings in overt behaviors noted in relation to disease, divorce, desertion or other social symptom

The main viewpoint has been directed toward the married adult, the paradigm emphasized for greatest social approval. The unmarried adults have been neglected.

It is because of the failure to face the problems of this large unmarried section of the community specifically that this volume has been undertaken. The various contributors are concerned with focussing attention upon the sexual problems of those living in unmarriage as contrasted with the married. They aim to consider all the facts that are ascertainable, to reveal the significant factors that can be determined, and above all to discuss the sexual problems of the unmarried adult honestly and with full recognition that the unmarried exist as an essential group in our civilization.

The unmarried possess the potentials of the married group to which they are definitely related by interest and participation in all the phases of life that affect the well-being of the married group. Their sex life, in its various forms, is vital to social welfare, just as it is significant for their own personal growth and development. Admittedly, to study this phase of sex is to explore one of the uncharted areas of our civilization in which the residua of barbaric ignorance and fear still retard progress. Over its depths appears an uninviting, miasmatic haze of doubt and uncertainty. Few organized explorations have been made of this state of unmarriage. Hence this effort to make a survey of the field from various angles represents an effort to chart facts, to trace causal influences, to determine the validity and worth of current views, and to establish data and hypotheses which may be of service in interpreting our age.

The essence of life is movement, and growth and reproduction. Protoplasm reproduces itself but the life of protoplasm is not limited to its reproductive phase. Man's sexual life is not limited to procreation nor is his power of creation the sole force affecting his self-directed life. The state of being human is common to the married and the unmarried. To be human is to be identified with a species of the animal kingdom. Sexual organization, sexual physiology, sexual psychology and sexual experience—mating, love, and erotic behavior—are not phenomena isolated for any group of animals, wed or unwed. Hence the sex life of unmarried adults commands a position no less important for all human beings than that which is accepted and recognized as pertaining and belonging to those living in wedlock.

If this book casts some light upon this meaningful territory of human vitality and activity, its purpose will have been fulfilled. If it broadens and extends his knowledge, man will have more understanding of his own human characteristics and greater insight into the world in which he lives and loves.

IRA S. WILE, M.D.

# CONTENTS

# THE SEX LIFE OF THE
# UNMARRIED ADULT

# INTRODUCTION

> That which distinguishes man from the beast is drinking without being thirsty and making love at all seasons.—PIERRE BEAUMARCHAIS

## IS THERE A SPECIAL SEX LIFE OF THE UNMARRIED ADULT?

*Ira S. Wile, M.D.*

LECTURER ON DISORDERS OF CONDUCT AND PERSONALITY, COLUMBIA UNIVERSITY

MANKIND IS the sole animal whose sexual instinct is not completely subjected to or totally regulated by rutting cycles. His mating proclivities are subject to his own sapient controls and those proclaimed by the group to which he belongs. For more than two thousand years the official gratification of procreative urges has been relegated to the socially recognized state of marriage. The assumption of society has been that its authoritative prohibition of the biologic mating urge would postpone its utilization until such a time as the requisite civil or religious rite gave sanction to its usage. If society expected external regulations to subjugate physiologic urges and psychologic impulses, have these regulations been effective? Do those living in unmarriage live in chastity and celibacy? If not, wherein and how do their sexual behaviors differ from those exhibited by fellow beings similar in all else except for living in marriage?

Fundamental urges cannot be destroyed without disintegrating personality. Sexual activity is not an isolated act—it is a general experience motivating and affecting personality. Out of the total personal reaction emerges ideas of romance and beauty, exaltation and peacefulness, devotion and slavish idealization; or, a sense of sacrifice, tumult, humiliation, shame, anxiety, a desire for self-punishment, or a self-accepted weakness, failure and inadequacy. The concept of "falling in love" may apply to self, to members of one's own or the opposite sex. There is usually a second personality that facilitates one's own growth in terms of sex impulses utilized for personal life. This is true for the unmarried no less than for the married, although society makes the adjustment a challenge, a propriety, a question. Havelock Ellis, referring to the play functions of sex, remarks, "The functions of sex on the psychic and emotional side are of far greater extention than any act of procreation, they may even exclude it altogether, and when we are concerned with the welfare of the individual human being we must enlarge our outlook and deepen our insight."

Normal beings have some basic plan in their sex life whether it be lived in anticipation, in phantasy, or in experience. This exists because life is unified and sex is not a thing or a force apart from the synthesis. Life may be a constant conflict between instinct and culture, but sexual powers and potentials serve the self even more than society from birth to death, in and out of marriage. What is the natural and normal tendency and reaction of an individual may be deemed abnormal because out of harmony with the standards of normality accepted by the group.

To interpret the sex life of the unmarried one must

recognize that there are two functions of sex: one, the biologic, with procreation as a goal—involving some intellectual but more emotional processes in the interest of race perpetuation. The other function consists of the promotion of social growth through human relationships. This involves the play function and erotic activity, with or without a procreative goal. There are two bases for the energy of the sexual drive—one, conscious, directed, guided, subjected to ethical controls; the other, unconscious, instinctual, impulsive, reacting to stimuli, but not subject to reason. Two social values are obvious in sex practices—one is the creation of a social economic unity in some family structure; the other involves the basic racial and national controls of individuals in terms of morals and ethics. These lead to two forms of differentiation of sexual activity—one having social sanction as marriage and unmarriage in terms of age and sex, with variations in the light of an advancing physiologic development in adolescence and its slow decline after the climacteric to senescent impotence. The other form has a social recognition without sanction, which at times tacitly accepts homosexual or other non-creative sexual behaviors and formulates blanket regulations for personal concealment of all active interests and practices contrary to social demands. In human beings sexual energy is manifest in two phases that serve the ego: one is as an essential component impressive upon the development of the organism physically and psychically; the other is expressive as a trait functionally reflective of the personality.

Eating from the tree of knowledge led Adam and Eve to know "that they were naked." Thus modesty and shame came into being and Paradise was lost. From this originated the concept of sensuality and the woman became responsible for Adam's fall. Love life is not limited to the married nor to the adult, nor can the desire for affection and its manifest expression be effaced by a flaming sword, legislation, or social code. In ancient and mediæval days the unmarried were less free in their activities and less secure against natural and unnatural penalties for illegal sex indulgence. The female was a chattel, and sex a commodity. This practice is fading. The age of science and its growing liberating values, the advance in learning and the increasing knowledge concerning the nature of sex and the modes of controlling all its hazards have brought about a greater personal security. This modern factor has tended to offset the older inhibitory trend born of passive acceptance of the idea of ignorance, sin and social subservience laid down in Genesis. Conscience has been hard pressed by science.

Celibacy as a form of God-like life was not readily secured by religious insistence, as witness the papal demand that it be an absolute rule of discipline for ministers in 385 A.D., and the statement of Hardouin, Bishop of Angers, in 1428, that licentiousness had become so habitual among the clergy that it was no longer reputed to be a sin. And the scandalous lives of the unmarried adult clergy fostered the progress of the Reformation. The early church was deeply interested in sexual matters, especially marriage and *crescite et multiplicamini*, including definite ideas concerning virginity and celibacy, mainly based upon the generic concept that all sex expression is sinful.

Paul, forsaking his free Greek beliefs, in a loose and licentious age, narrowed and debauched the idea of sex. "He that is unmarried is careful for the things of the Lord, how he may please the Lord, but he that is married is careful for the things of the world, how he may please his wife and is divided." Sex life was made anathema, though it was "better to marry than burn." With his eyes closed to reality, Paul, with masculine absorption, assumed that all the other unmarried men, like him, would reject and take no thought of women—daughters of Eve and tempting emissaries of the Devil. Celibacy played its part in the lives of vestal virgins, wizards and witches, monks and nuns, and some priests and priestesses, but sexual thinking and acting were not lacking among those who became Brides of Christ or were mystically and ecstatically united with Him.

Love was the work of the Devil, and his phallic agents, *incubi* and *succubi,* rushed hither and thither seducing innocent human victims. As Martin Delrio, a Jesuit, declared: "Fascination is a power, derived from a pact with the devil." The evil eye fascinated, and weak souls needed a protection equally mystic. That which was natural in sex became degrading, and evil and its negation through chastity became a religious ideal. Tertullian thought virginity the peak of a spiritual life and the church sought its own desexualization and protection against the inherent wickedness of females, "the Devil's gateway." Woman, according to St. Chrysostom, was "a necessary evil, a natural temptation, a desirable calamity, a deadly fascination, and a painted ill." St. Athanasius noted that "What God did to Mary is the glory of all virgins; for they are attached as virginal saplings to her who is root." And St. Ambrose did not hesitate to proclaim, "From Eve we inherited damnation through the fruit of the tree." Love was to be spiritualized. Earthly satisfactions were to be sacrificed for heavenly joys. Women were to be inferiors, dependent upon man and subject to their husbands, even as urged recently by Pope Pius XI in his *De Connubis.*

The principle of chastity, tangled up in ideas of shame, modesty, decency, morals and life-hereafter, lay at the foundation of Pauline Christianity. The church still emphasizes it in varying degree, but with more understanding of the weakness of the doctrine as compared with the strength of the urge it sought to restrain. Many primitive people preferred unchastity among their potential wives as a guarantee of fertility; these included African natives as well as some Indian Tribes of America, Peru, New Zealand, and the Philippine Islands. Chastity itself has not been universal in its appeal to the unmarried, nor is it today. While procreation was viewed as a most holy function, it was held to involve descent into sinful sensuality. Marriage was the resort of the unmarried to secure release for illicit passion through a sanctioned indulgence—the right way for wrong doing.

Situational thinking and action enter into practical living. Neither an impossible theory nor a showy acceptance of a social veneer can disguise the substance of native patterns of action. Our age is one of realism, derived in revolt against romantic, idealistic illusions of a past generation. The exaltation of chastity and celibacy as goals of life has diminished. The available data indicate that unmarried adults have not subscribed by action to the dicta of their induced conscience and the prescribed ideal behavior.

The friendly status of widows, the popular social acceptance of divorce, the gaiety of male worshippers of Venus, the non-segregation of prostitutes and the financial advantages of mistresses have culminated during recent years in nervous and unhappy discussions of youth flaming, with considerable heat and more light.

The erotic play of a younger generation is, however, reflected at all ages in a greater freedom of all relations between the sexes. A new culture pattern reflects a new generation, but not necessarily its degeneration.

We are far from the era of romance in hoopskirts, bustles or corsets; wasp-waists and bell skirts are as extinct as hanging baskets of flowers; and hitching posts have sped away along with horse cars and tobacco juice. Spooning has been activated into petting, and necking —light and heavy—has taken its place. Gone are bundling, husking bees and post office; sex play is too frank to require specious excuses for its existence.

Natural selection is ever functioning in terms of appearance, form, odor, sex consciousness, sex attraction and sex appreciation. The unmarried vary in types, with quantitative rather than qualitative differences. The sex drive exists and its mode of expression depends upon time, place and circumstance, as well as upon basic structure and psychologic makeup. There are marked distinctions between extroverts and introverts, with reference to their reactions toward their erotic potentials and their utilization of them. The extrovert is readily swayed emotionally and is responsive to all people, while the introvert, self-consciously sensitive and preoccupied with self, tends to repress all free emotional expression. The urgency of sexual demands and the pressure of interests, at once centripetal and centrifugal, determine a style of life that will vary in terms of effects upon total happiness. The potent may be sated by amatory quests and become impotent. The impotent may find new life from a revised technique of functional esthetics. Some lives are blasted by the recollections of early errors that preclude later normal sexual activity. Attitudes toward sex thus reflect attitudes toward life itself. This becomes more evident in those whose fears lead to inhibitions, to an ashamed bashfulness in wooing, or to a frigidity that wrecks marriage. It is equally true among those who live on an auto-erotic level or those who find their satisfactions in homosexual liaisons.

Fear of venereal diseases and fear of pregnancy were held to be barriers to sexual intimacies, although they served perhaps no more successfully than did modesty and religious convictions. One must distinguish the amorous propensity from a desire for propagation. Erotic desire is not synonymous with sexual activity. Sexual enthusiasm does not disappear when procreative capacity ceases at the climacteric. The unmarried are not especially interested in conception, save negatively. Primitive people do not link love-making with reproduction. They do not always connect the amatory processes with the genitalia. The erotic play that designedly involves genital responses differs from other forms. The distinctions made in petting recognize that erotic activity may or may not have coitus as a goal. The Watsonian conceives the development of love as a specialized growth of touch. The sex play of the unmarried, even when unconcerned with courtship, involves all forms of touch, including hand-holding, osculation, body pressures and dancing, as well as the less dynamic behaviors of conversation and going to the theatre—or concert, or canoeing by moonlight.

Social conventions and regulations alter the prevailing modes of sex activity as they do the styles for hats and calling cards. Every particular age has its own preferred sex styles, but today, as ever, one finds individual variations from timorous asceticism to boastful promiscuity. Our mechanical era has stressed education and contraception more than the liturgies and commandments. Sex has been glorified in terms of its non-physical values. Modesty has yielded to discretion, and sexual tension has been released to offset the horrors allegedly threatened by suppression, as well as repression. At times those rejecting all sex play feel that they are on the defensive; that their ethical concepts endanger their social success and their peace of mind.

Occasionally virtuous living is based upon defensive statements that raise questions of personal fear concerning virility or frigidity, inherent homosexuality or anxiety over a tendency to some abnormal practice that is non-existent save as a threat and an inhibiting idea. There are those who fear sex as though it were immediately self-destructive. Others struggle in vain against a sense of inferiority from micro-sexual development. Some are loyal to their idealized lovers, or to their fixated incestuous wishes, or to their obsessive attachment to older people of the same or opposite sex. Some are caught up in religious dedications or are celibate by conviction. Others merely await the right person and, until then, they seek relief in phantasy or cling to the career motive. Some few believe they are sublimating by a studied devotion to art and creative efforts. Among all these types, however, the sexual life is not static, and masturbatory activity vies with phantasy in balancing tensions that stir the entire being. Morality is not established by the mere denial of psycho physical pressures. The adult is the result of his past life and sex experience is not completely lacking.

Numerous studies have disclosed that the unmarried, like the married, have varied sex experiences. Klatt found that 18 per cent of women had some active form of experience under 18 years, and 60.6 per cent between 18 and 22 years. Among Hamilton's selected professional group, 59 per cent of the men and 47 per cent of the women had had coitus before marriage, and 20 per cent of the males and 16 per cent of the females, before 21 years of age.

Katherine B. Davis, studying the sex life of 1,200 unmarried college women, reported 61 per cent admitting masturbation, of whom 57 per cent began before age 15 years. Sex feelings and desire were experienced with some periodicity in 70 per cent of the group reporting on this. The unmarried, no less than the married, reported various forms of sexual phenomena. It is interesting to note that homosexual relations were reported more frequently for the unmarried group. This is significant even though, socially, homosexuality is regarded as more dangerous among men than among women. Much homosexuality among males ceases with confidence in heterosexual potency, as confirmed in mating followed by marriage. Lesbianism is common and its prevalence is important though it does not always involve remaining single. The single group regretted the lack of children more than the lack of husbands. Approximately 38.7 per cent believed intercourse necessary for complete mental and physical health. Approximately 20 per cent justified sexual intercourse before marriage for men and for women. This reflects an attitude that has become more prevalent during the past decade.

If we divide people into the married and not-married, who constitute the latter group? Obviously it contains those who wish to be married and those who fear to be; those who should not, those who must not, those who cannot and those who may not; and those who can and may but reject marriage because of some specific factor, or are still in hopes of attaining matrimonial recognition. Among those who cannot or may not, there are physical defectives; chronic sufferers from disease, contagious or devitalizing; mental incompetents; the economically dependent; and those ethically and religiously opposed, as well as those legally handicapped by age or color. Some may not marry because they are institutionalized as criminals, defectives, psychotics, psychoneurotics and dependents. But do all of these live asexually? Those charged with the care of this group appreciate the extent of the sexual problems bound up in segregation and isolation.

The early mature groups, the generally unmarried section of the population, and those divorced or widowed constitute a large and normal part of our population. According to the U. S. Bureau of Census in 1930, 34.1 per cent of males over 15 years were single, 4.6 per cent widowed and 1.1 per cent divorced. Of the females 26.4 per cent were single, 11.1 per cent widowed and 1.3 divorced. It is verly significant that figures for the marital condition of the population of the United States are based upon persons 15 years old and older. The government thus acknowledges maturity in the procreative potentials of a group not legally accepted as adult in other directions. The United States Department of Education regards sixteen-year-olds as adult. It is absurd to think of this group as differing sexually from those in marriage, despite all the possible factors that inhere in marital covenants.

Are the large numbers of adult single undergraduates and graduates of colleges endowed with less sexual drive than high school graduates? Do matured adolescents lose their primary instinctive urges when they become adult? Is higher education purchased at the cost of sexual contraction? This is absurd and contrary to all facts. Sexual activity in one of its many phases exists—whether in active erotic play, auto-erotic, homosexual or heterosexual practice, or as an esthetic or vocational sublimation. Its nature and intensity are subject to personal choice, judgment, standards, and ideals which are regulative but not destructive—temporarily prohibitive rather than permanently inhibitive.

If one assumes that sexual life is and must be limited by social sanction to those living in wedlock, then what do those living in unmarriage do or what may they do? The question is not what can they do, as this is identical for both groups. The actual legal existence of prenuptial guarantees attests the fact of widespread sexual activity among the unmarried. The military data concerning prophylactic stations and the facts concerning unmarried mothers offer occasion for deliberation. This is further witnessed by all available statistics for venereal diseases, illegitimacy, abortion, prostitution, rape and other sexual assaults. The traditional sex life of the sailors, with a love in every port, is not inherently different from that of the land-lubbers who also travel in company with Eros.

Being adult depends upon biologic and social definitions. Social recognition of the capacity for propagation concedes a preparedness for heterosexual activity. Hence, there should be less surprise at its occurrence, especially when the common law minimum marriage licensing age is 14 years for boys and 12 for girls. This legally obtains in ten states. The highest statutory minimum licensing age is in New Hampshire—20 years for boys and 18 years for girls. In eight states, Idaho, Kentucky, New York, North Carolina, Texas, Utah, Vermont and the District of Columbia, it is 16 for boys and 14 for girls. Are those still unmarried at ages above these necessarily less adult, or are those married below 21 years merely children? The voting age is not biological, nor does it determine adult behavior, sexual experience or marriage.

Economic inadequacy does not stamp out heterosexual urges any more than the enactment of a punitive law can destroy homosexual impulses. Factually, society recognizes the sexual demands, if not the sexual needs, of the unmarried group in its attitudes toward, and its regulation of, prostitution, homosexual haunts and taxi dance halls. Society appraises sex habits and approves of standards for the sexes. These have shifted with the altered status of women. Judgment, in the form of legal decisions, is formulated concerning the nature and meaning of sexual normality and abnormality. Society rejects as perverts: masturbators, homosexuals, voyeurs, exhibitionists, sadists and masochists, especially if the young and the unmarried are involved. A perversion of function is any form of sexual activity that does not intrinsically foster procreation.

The idea of the sexual necessity for males obtained for a long time, and the lack of sexual expression was considered responsible for many personality disorders, neuroses and psychoneuroses. In psychopathology, sex plays a significant part, apparently more so among the unmarried than among those wedded. But as the Bureau of Census properly noted: "This is not to be interpreted as indicating that the single are more liable to become insane than the married. It means rather that the insane as compared with the normal are less likely to marry." Similarly one must differentiate between concomitance and causality, in passing upon the relation of sex life to all forms of psychopathy. As psychoneurotics are uncommon among primitive people, part of the explanation of its prevalence among the civilized may rest upon the ideas of sin, guilt, shame and disgust, which arose from social forces crystallized in conscience.

It is socially significant that there were 34.1 per cent of males over 15 years, and 26.4 per cent females, single in 1930 as compared with 41.7 per cent and 31.8 per cent in 1890. Our reversion to more primitive and more honest attitudes toward sex and sex play undoubtedly has brought about a considerable part of this decrease of the unmarried in the population. This is also evident in the birth rate in 1928, when 1.3 births per 1,000 born were by mothers 10–14 years, and 119 to mothers 15–19 years. Erotic play has become an end rather than a means, while masculine dominance has diminished in the realm of sexual activity. The process of democratization of sex life has proceeded along with the development of women's rights. The attainment of suffrage gave a greater political equality to a new woman—mainly new only because she sloughed off some traditions, taboos and timidities and put into practice what had always been a lurking wish. Many a woman had wished a child, though not a husband, and many had hoped for a mate without a marriage, while still others had longed for masculine opportunities and seized them.

Procreation has always possessed economic value. Children were assets in an agricultural civilization based upon hand power; in an industrial mechanized world they became liabilities. Conception, despite every beautiful social theory, rarely was purposefully undertaken in the interest of the state. When purpose entered, it served the parents for personality values or other gain. The regulation of child-bearing became imperative, and voluntary limitation of offspring was practiced—at first through abortions and, as knowledge increased, through contraception. The rights of parents and children in terms of economic-social survival created a new and more rational outlook upon life. The greatly reduced and still diminishing birth rate tells its own story. As the size of the family decreases, there is a greater similarity in the meaning of all sexual activity, whether in or out of wedlock.

The diminished group of present-day adolescents approaching adult levels have had greater opportunities for personal growth. The highly developed code of personal liberty has permeated their system of thought. They have taken over the idea of personality growth, life enrichment and the right to self-regulation. A heightened education, a more scientific outlook, a freer discussion of physical hygiene, mental hygiene, sex hygiene, social hygiene, a more open discussion of companionate marriage, divorce, contraception, venereal diseases, perversions—and life is organized for sexual thinking and acting upon a plane that would have been interdicted, if not impossible, a generation ago. But all generations have changed and grandmothers are competing with grandchildren for greater erotic freedoms.

In an industrial organization, the status of the female as a responsive being has changed more than that of the male. She is now a worker outside of her home. The nature of female occupation merits attention, especially in the light of the generally lower wage scale for females as compared with males. In 1930 there were 10,632,227 women in all occupations, of whom 5,734,825 were single, 1,826,100 widowed and divorced. What were the sex problems of the 1,863,766 single women 20–25 years of age? Or of the 1,911,159 single women 25–44 years of age, not to mention the 1,436,715 women 15–19 years old? Is it possible that their preoccupation with earning sublimated their sexual life! The number of illegitimate births during 1928 was 31,657 to women of 15–19 years, 18,185 to those 20–24 years, 6,004 to those 25–29 years, and even 558 to women of 40–45 years. Half of these births were among Negroes, but the figures are meager at best and cannot be interpreted save in terms of the total number of pregnancies with births averted—and such data are unavailable. More important, perhaps, is the fact that despite increasing contraceptive knowledge, the ratio of socially illegitimate and biologically legitimate births to the total number of births per thousand rose from 24.0 in 1926 to 30.9 in 1928.

What is the sublimating content of domestic and personal service in which two-thirds of the 3,166,603 female workers were not married? Are the lives of laundresses, practical nurses, cooks and waitresses happily chaste in thought and deed? What is the sex-denying factor in agriculture, in which more than one-half of the women were not married, or the two-thirds of those in manufacturing and mechanical industries or in trade, or the four-fifths of the women in clerical work? Fatigue may restrain, while lack of interest may stimulate, amativeness and its expression in some form. The opportunity for being with men, propinquity in working and struggling alongside of them, involves the possibility of loving and living with them for an hour or a lifetime. Many add to the joy of life by adventure, by desire for affection, by need of social expansions. Others, appreciating that marriage might not release them from toil and struggle for security, prefer to risk happiness in mating without responsibility rather than enter into a shaky, if not perilous, economic partnership not easily dissolved. And there is no necessity for stressing possible auto-erotic or homosexual behavior, though these may have economic roots just as did such practices as concubinage, polygamy and polyandry.

There were 1,525,960 women in professional life of whom only 294,297 were married. Are these actresses, authors, teachers, musicians, doctors, lawyers and nurses asexual? What of this group in unmarriage? Are they self-doomed to the denial of their feminine natures as potential creators? Does professional life satisfy every biologic need? Are professional women lacking in heterosexual urges any more than their professional brethren? Desire is not extinguished by professional activity, though it may be banked by constant duties. The choice of marriage or a career does not involve a choice between mating and a career. The choice of marriage merely requires an adjustment to certain concepts of permanent relations on a plane of economic subservience and social loyalties to one man. Studies such as those of Hamilton, Davis and Dickinson indicate that these adjustments are readily made.

The problem thus stated for women has more force today since it is no longer held that the powerful male must be the sole support of the family. Mating and marrying have less distinction when the partnership idea enters into the total lives of two persons. This is even more true when pregnancy is to be avoided until conception is desired by the partners. They merge and emerge more easily, hence the trend toward earlier marriage and easier divorce or trial marriage, theoretical companionate marriage and mating without rites.

There is no essential biologic distinction between the married and the unmarried, unless some biologic deviation is responsible for non-marriage or is the sole determiner of homosexual activities. Social, ethical, moral and religious factors are inherent in many fields of work, and their restraint values are specific rather than generic. Social laws and conventions must be personally accepted to possess validity for the guidance of sexual life. These often vary in society and in some groups composing it, as among the intelligentsia, artists, musicians, sailors, Bohemians, hoboes, prisoners and professional groups of various types. Biologic rather than economic values now appear to be prevailing, while the personal significance of sexual factors transcends the social implications of marriage.

The fact that biology and economics are less closely bound and that problems of child-bearing have altered rather to child-rearing, when such becomes necessary, is evidenced in the fact that the proportion of gainfully occupied women, 15 years and older, who are married, had increased from 13.9 per cent in 1890 and 15.4 per cent in 1900 to 28.9 per cent in 1930. Similarly it is noteworthy that the proportion of married women 15 years and older gainfully employed rose from 4.6 per cent in 1890 to 5.6 per cent in 1900, to 11.7 per cent in 1930. The increasing independence of woman has lessened her sexual as well as her economic dependence upon any one man. Social law operates as ever but with fewer threats and less intense penalties. Women have taken over the freedoms formerly held to be the sole prerogative of the males. The word "obey" is fading from the marriage service. Part of the badly worn moral veneer has cracked and an alert generation has recognized its own biologic substance and has termed this recognition sex liberalism. Liberalism may mean an enslavement as well as a liberation; and the distinction lies in whether sensuality or sensuousness dominates in adapting the expression and fulfillment of personal needs in the light of total living values.

Sexual behaviors result in part from contiguity, if not contagion, in different social settings. It is not without meaning that in the United States there were a million more males than females in 1930, and that single females predominated in rural farm areas while single males were excessive in urban areas. Man or woman in isolation is subjected to reactions and possibilities, unnecessary, if not impossible, in the midst of companionships. But the rustic bumpkin and the sophisticated city rounder are brothers in sex urges and desires. Their social habits, including erotic tendencies, may be coarse or idealized, poetic or prosaic, dependent upon the nature and nurture of their active human relationships. Hence modesty and shame geographically have varying values. A primitive Susannah would merely have turned her head aside while bathing if conscious of prying elders. A primitive elder would not have pried upon a maid in her ablutions.

Shame was not always attached to intercourse. Husbands once were privileged to lend their wives to others; girls were offered experience with males; temple prostitution, like orgiastic fertility ceremonies, contained no element of immodesty, shame or stigma. The cohabitation of boys and girls was natural among Australian primitives, and amorous pleasures were accepted as belonging to the life of the young, even while many reservations were being made for those married. Even the establishment of monogamy as an ideal failed to overcome all earlier trends to sexual freedom and experimentation.

Monogamy as a legal matter and monogamy in practice and custom reflect different ideas. There is ample reason to doubt the complete and literal reality of monogamy among peoples professing it most sincerely.

This is suggested in the liberalizing of the divorce laws, the changing attitudes toward unmarried mothers and the light approach given to the subject of adultery. Sex morality changes as does all else. Love and marriage are not identical in nature and goals and often are in actual conflict. Familial regulation for economic and social purposes would emphasize marriage, but factually there is a growing stress upon love in the interest of individual personality growth. After the rejection of concubinage, morality was held to be inherent in marriage, but today it is deemed to rest upon the dynamic interrelations of individuals entering into matrimony.

The happy absorption of people in and by marriage has become a newer criterion of marriage success. For this reason there has been a growing tendency to test relationships and compatibilities in physical activity, intellectual interests, social intimacies and emotional adjustments through sexual experimentation along practical lines believed to foster later marital felicity. A knowledge of sexual compatibility has assumed a primary value, perhaps unwarrantedly appearing to guarantee later marital permanency. This, however, is not an isolated modification of the mores. It is in line with the opening of smoking rooms in colleges for girls, the scantification of attire, the greater frankness in smutty story and blasphemy, the fearless hitch-hiking, the social approval of cocktail parties, the gay party crashing, and the open unchaperoned fêtes in apartments of either sex.

*C'est la guerre d'amour*—and all treaties are scrapped. The War itself was a factor in breaking down modesty, when female society was organized to protect soldiers against exposure to prostitutes and the venereal diseases, and young women sold their kisses patriotically with Liberty Bonds. The bonds went, the liberty remained—the morals of the war continue.

Our standards of morality have changed even as our manners. De Tocqueville rightfully noted: "Thus not only a democratic people cannot have aristocratic manners, but they neither comprehend nor desire them; and as they have never thought of them, it is to their minds as if such things had never been. Too much importance should not be attached to this loss, but it may well be regretted." The double standard of morality was aristocratic and the single standard more democratic. Its force lies in the implication that there shall be no distinctions in the privileges and rights for the sexes. Males shall have no monopoly of sexual privilege. A coerced marriage is no longer the basis of feminine sexual morality. Ellen Key said: "Love thus becomes more and more a private affair of the individual while children are more and more the business of society." This is not an entirely new view, as the Courts of Love held that marriage and love were mutually exclusive.

The practice of continued sexual abstinence may strengthen or destroy individuals, just as sensuality and grossness in or out of marriage may bring about a physical and spiritual deterioration. The modern conception of standard practice is well exemplified by T. W. Galloway: "On purely *physiological* grounds there is no reason why temperate sex intercourse should be allowed in marriage and denied to the unmarried. Marriage makes no difference whatever in physiology. *It is to be frankly admitted therefore that any grounds for sexual abstinence of people, younger or older, are not biological but social, esthetic and ethical.* This does not mean that they are any less compelling." They are less compelling than a decade ago. The uncertainties of life the loss of earlier anchorages and a lack of knowledge of the present drift of the social current have made the enjoyment of a complete life seem more important than a self-control in the interest of a dubious promise of satisfaction in marriage.

Love is difficult to control because of the biologic influences of sex attractiveness and attraction. Man as a group endeavors to regulate what man as an individual finds difficult. Hence social conventions and taboos are severe, often harsh and pitiless. Codes seek to block urgent passion in the interest of appearance, decency, public morality. Natural law may have ruled the universe, but not since gregarious human beings united in some communal group and reasoned sex into a set of restricted habits and practices, varying from the *lex primae noctis* to "to have and to hold, until death doth us part." When free mating was supplanted by the concept of "whom God had joined together," there arose a greater consciousness of apparel, osculation, tumescence, wickedness and immorality. Marriage after publication of the banns could not destroy love-making and clandestine courtship any more than could scarlet letters, fines and imprisonment. Excessive Puritanic legislation defeated its own purpose, and the demonstration of the past is again manifest in the revolt against hypocrisy and a threatened discipline based upon the idea that sex in and of itself is evil, traducing and debasing. The growing freedoms of today have emanated as a protest against the prolonged social endeavor to make all sex shameful, fearful, unholy and unclean. Prohibition has declined in influence in favor of rational guidance in the light of biologic principles.

The health of men and women is concerned with vitality and power. Active desire and potential realization are accepted as normal. Virility and impotence are not equally approved. Maturation is founded upon the development of the capacity to beget. Social living is based upon responsible sexual realization. Adult life is based upon an integration of the personality in which genital organization and sexual urge are ever operative. The histories of unmarried psychoneurotics and psychotics, the lives of nervous people living in sexual phantasies, trying to escape the stern realities of daily living, leave no uncertainty concerning the normalizing and stabilizing values of normal living in terms of physiologic and psychologic endowment. The social value of virginity is not biologically founded, and the biologic values of celibacy are not social. The principles of sex denial, hypocritic concealment and the self-degradation of sex in any form serve no stabilized personal goals. Prudishness fortunately is giving way to frankness; and nudism attests the superiority of revelation for personal control, as opposed to the salacity of imagination at the artificialities of dressing—mainly designed to enhance sexual values and to be beautiful incitements to appreciation, if not lures for aggressive admiration.

The fundamental biologic difference of the sexes disappears in their unity as part of a creative system. So long as the sexual differentiations were viewed as essential, and female functions were regarded primarily as existing for service to men, the richest relations of the sexes in equality were impossible. Familial arrangements for betrothal and marriage could occur while the prospective matrimonial partners were being cradled. Purchase price and marriage by capture told much of the status of the affections, when there was no need for a master to win the love of the creature he chose for his gratification and service, after due rites and ceremonies. Sexual life and love are not exactly alike, save in the Freudian sense, but what De Tocqueville said of marriage holds true for relations among the unmarried. "When a man always chooses a wife for himself, without any external coercion or even guidance, it is generally a conformity of tastes and opinions which brings a man and a woman together, and this same conformity keeps and fixes them in close habits of intimacy." It is this freedom of choice that now prevails, but no longer is it always the man who chooses.

Marriage is a social term relating to a relationship between one or more men to one or more women in accordance with a recognized and accepted custom or law. The marriage of two in permanent monogamy is the present accepted pattern of love relations. The institution involves rights and duties for the contracting parties and establishes a status for any resulting offspring. Legally, sexual consummation is the binding element, and non-intercourse offers grounds for annulment. Religiously, the sacrament is sexual realization. Sexual failure represents the theoretic continuation of the state of unmarriage. The implication remains that coitus is a privilege of the married only. This concept is rejected by society as fact, even though it endeavors to force a marriage to legitimatize offspring. This is on a par with the Southern Bambala of the Congo who regard marriage as a definite affair only when a child is expected. Similarly, in Borneo there is free intercourse so long as pregnancy is avoided; if it occurs marriage is required.

This clearly connotes that if there be no issue, society need not be especially concerned with the sexual activity. Today one hears this opinion openly expressed as the basis of much of the more open relationships among the unmarried. There are those who go further and demand that every woman have the right to one child, with no questions asked. Obviously, this is difficult while the economic value of marriage is tied up with laws of inheritance in a capitalistic system under a patrilineal society.

The unmarried group are as concerned as the married with biology, sociology, economics, psychology, medicine, law and morals as related to personal living. They sense new values and face their responsibilities honestly. Unknowingly, they have precipitated a crisis—just another of the many crises of the world "going to the demnition bow-wows." Their pattern of action is that of the male members of more uncivilized races who seek to marry as soon after puberty as possible, or of the civilized males who are expected to marry at a definite age, as among the Orthodox Jews the Rabbis urged marriage at eighteen years at the latest. Indeed, capable men who refused to marry at age 20 often were compelled to do so by the Court. Under this scheme almost every female attains marriage. The exceptions to marriage are generally only the physically deformed, the idiots, epileptics, the workers of magic and the psychic inverts. As Prescott noted of the Dakota Indians, "I do not know of a bachelor among them. They have a little more respect for women and themselves, than to live a single life." This idea is reflected in the Kafir's judgment that a permanently unmarried woman "must be a hopelessly bad character." Among many people, like the Hindoos, it is a disgrace for a family to contain an unmarried girl who is marriageable; that is, sexually and socially mature.

The history of man indicates the more natural mating and consequent marriage age as occurring in terms of biologic capacity and social readiness. This holds true despite a certain prevalence of child marriage, which means below fourteen and twelve years for boys and girls respectively. The marriage form has always been in harmony with the mores of the age and people as related to the economics of family organization.

The history of marriage involves the history of unmarriage and both are conditioned by changing mores, which affect doctrines of endogamy and exogamy, polygamy and polyandry, trial and term marriage, permanent or consecutive monogamy, as well as infanticide, abortion and contraception. The mores affect and are in turn subject to majority ideas concerning virginity and celibacy, marriage by purchase or by free choice, adultery or social paramour, mating and prostitution. Biologically, sexual urges and procedures are imperative and limited to a comparatively few productive and nonproductive forms of expression. Socially, sexual function may be subject to an unlimited variety of compulsive though elastic regulations, adapted to what is deemed the social good. This is the norm for decency of personal living and applies to the unmarried as it defines their status with relation to the married. The norm, however, alters as, socially, man tends to change; and unwillingness to conform constitutes the dynamic basis of the conflict between generations.

What the future of marriage is to be is conjectural. It may not be our present form of monogamy. It is probable, however, that the more freely marriage is encouraged, the earlier it will occur; and the earlier it occurs, the less significant will become the sexual problems of the unmarried. The deviations from heterosexual activities common among civilized peoples are rare among more primitive peoples, who have few problems concerning their unmarried adults. The Trobriand Islanders, for example, have a general taboo of all aberrations of the sexual impulse, as well as upon "publicity and lack of decorum in sexual matters."

The sex life of the unmarried adult is varied in terms of personal goals, of biologic need, and social adjustment. It is freer today because life is freer. There is a growing acceptance of the sexual rights and practices among the older group of the unmarried. Our people are more independent and have been subject to an economic inflation that gave materialistic ideas a highly individualistic slant. Religious forces have become less binding and the sanctions of the church have become less effective. Marriage was one expression of a material relationship into which religious values had been injected, when sex itself was rejected. The inevitable swing of the moral pendulum occurred and the spiritual values of sexual life came to have new meaning and value in terms of companionship, love and emotional security and personal fulfillment. The romance idea still lingers, although arrogant rebels against conventional sex regulations would deny it with romantic indignation.

Just as the Lambeth Conference of Anglican Bishops gave consideration to polygamy as a means of repopulating England after the war, and then recently gave partial approval to contraceptive practices, so the moral ideas of individuals have altered concerning their sexual activities. The broad modern policies of the Young Women's Christian Association in offering courses on sexual problems, the approval of the Catholic Church of an alleged safe period for non-fecundative intercourse, and the growth of college courses on marriage, indicate that sexual life is being considered by men and women in a more intelligent manner. They are now concerned with positive ideas rather than negations, with values in the present life rather than in the hereafter.

Unmarried adults are approaching sex as a fact rather than a theory. They are accepting their sexual organization frankly as an instrument for personal growth and emotional completion with social stabilization, rather than hypocritically as a function designed by divine plan only for the procreation of pure beings whose excuse for living was that they might die in purity to attain happiness in a world to come. They appreciate that sex is the source of life, but believe that a sexless life is a mockery after biologic maturation, because it is contrary to nature. They concede that the social values of sex inhere in the psychological factors that socialize individuals and lead them to forsake unmarriage for a marriage in harmony with the laws and customs of their age. All erotic play is genetically related to courtship, but courtship is subject to social control. Hence, the sex life of the normal young unmarried adult, whatever it may be, is preparation for the perfection of mating and the promotion of personal happiness and adjustment in some form of marriage, whether free and unconventional, common-law or according to civil or religious rite.

# ANTHROPOLOGY

Man is endowed with sexual tendencies but these have to be moulded in addition by systems of cultural rules which vary from one society to another.—BRONISLAW MALINOWSKI

## THE SEX LIFE OF THE UNMARRIED ADULT IN PRIMITIVE SOCIETY

*Margaret Mead*
ASSISTANT CURATOR OF ETHNOLOGY,
AMERICAN MUSEUM OF NATURAL HISTORY,
NEW YORK CITY

IF AN unmarried adult be defined as an individual regarded by his society as socially mature and therefore of an age to be married, the unmarried adults in primitive society are almost entirely limited to the widowed, the maimed, the deformed, the diseased, the insane and the mentally deficient. While primitive societies vary in the degree to which they explicitly emphasize the point, to be socially mature is to be, among other things, married. Therefore, in most primitive societies such individuals are definitely social deviants, either through defect or special circumstances, so that a discussion of their rather bizarre situation is irrelevant in this symposium and, in a sense, invidious.

If we turn, however, to a consideration of the interval between sexual maturity and social maturity, the primitive material immediately assumes relevance, for very few primitive societies regard the two as coincident. However much early sexual promiscuity or child-betrothal is emphasized, the great majority of primitive societies demand of the boy who is to be married the ability to assume full economic responsibility for his wife and children; and of the girl, the strength to bear healthy children and the skill and judgment to rear them. In those societies where the family group consists of some dozen or more mature individuals who coöperate as parts of one economic unit—as in Samoa, Ontong Java, Zuni—although the husband may not assume individual responsibility for his family, nevertheless he and his wife are expected to be able to make an economic contribution equivalent to the additional strain which his wife and children put upon the resources of the large household.

Popular beliefs enormously overemphasize the prevalence of very early marriage among primitive peoples. The fact that almost everyone is married by the time he or she is twenty-one or twenty-two does not necessarily mean that anyone is married at sixteen. Primitive communities differ from modern communities not because children are married at puberty but because marriage for all individuals must take place when they arrive at a certain age, and after this there are no unmarried individuals.

Beliefs that all primitive people mature earlier than civilized people are also unfounded. As among individuals in modern society, there is a wide variation in the age of puberty, often not apparent to the observer because a people without age records define age itself in terms of physical development. In New Guinea, for instance, the age of women is commonly defined as: her breasts do not yet stand up; soon now her breasts will stand up; her breasts have stood up; and her breasts have now fallen down maturely. These four stages represent the periods from late childhood in which there is as yet no sign of puberty, and the three stages of puberty. Without any record of chronological age, a girl of ten will often be classified with a girl of fifteen. While there is some reliable evidence for very early puberty among some primitive peoples, there is also evidence from some societies of an average age of first menstruation which is later, rather than earlier, than among girls in modern civilization.

The majority of primitive societies, as well as the civilized, practice marriage; that is, they finally associate sexual activity with a definite and more or less permanent and public mating pattern in which children can be legally born and reared. The lack of inevitableness of this association can be seen in the social organization of the Nayars of Malabar, among whom sex and economic responsibility for children have been finally and completely dissociated in every respect. Nayar girls are married at a tender age, by a formal religious ceremony, and then immediately divorced; after this, it is impossible for them ever to marry again. They live on under the parents' roof, taking such lovers as they choose, and the children whom they bear remain as part of the mother's family, the father having no claim whatsoever. In Nayar society everyone is an unmarried adult with a full sex life and the question of illegitimacy vanishes. The problem of the division of responsibility between men and women in the rearing of children has been solved by making the kin of the mother provide for them instead of the father. Yet the presence of the elaborate pretense at a highly patrilineal marriage form and its dissolution shows that this is no primitive expression of matriliny and ignorance of the father's rôle.

This brings us to a consideration of one of the least easily explained and most widespread phenomena of primitive society, the lack of correlation between attitudes toward premarital freedom and attitudes toward premarital pregnancy. Primitive societies may be roughly divided into those societies in which girls are married at puberty, those in which girls marry at some time after puberty but to whom all sex relations are interdicted before marriage, and those in which girls marry some time after puberty but are permitted sex relations before marriage. In the last group there are many instances of complete social acceptance of premarital freedom, but this very seldom carries with it any approval of premarital pregnancy. The instance which shows most sharply the inconsistency of this attitude is the Trobriands, where native theory denies the facts of physical paternity. The social code permits complete sexual freedom before marriage and still it is disgraceful for a child to be born out of wedlock.

This disapproval of premarital pregnancy occurs among peoples with widely varying degrees of efficiency in the use of contraceptives and abortifacients. Briffault, in *The Mothers,* has criticized very cogently the inadequacy of using the scarcity of illegitimate children as proof of premarital chastity, by comparing infanticide in this situation with other formal types of infanticide, such as killing all children after the fourth, or all children born within a certain period. It is true that in those tribes where all that is required of an unmarried mother is sufficient discretion to kill her child quietly as soon as it is born, the social attitude which regards childlessness and promiscuity as compatible social patterns for unmarried girls is not unreasonable in its demands. But in many primitive societies, the requirement is not that the child shall not live but that the mother shall not be known to be pregnant. It seems almost as though marriage and pregnancy were an original fixed complex, and that the attitude toward pregnancy had held over long after marriage was deferred beyond puberty, or the chaperonage of youth was relaxed.

Whatever may be the cause, very few primitive societies take the point of view attributed to the Spartans, with their social recognition of the *parthenoi,* children born out of wedlock. It is far commoner to find, among those societies which permit premarital freedom, an extreme intolerance of pregnancy combined with a degree of license under which only the most expert contraception can ensure every girl the required barrenness. These facts can be interpreted to serve many theories of origins, of primitive promiscuity or primitive absence of knowledge of paternity, of a primordial failure to dissociate sex and parenthood, and so forth. All of these remain merely amusing speculations and are irrelevant here. It is sufficient to note the fact and stress the insistence of primitive society upon parenthood as being a dual responsibility shared by a member of each sex, even in those very aberrant societies, like the Nayars and the natives of Mentawei, where the father or the brother of the woman plays the social rôle usually accorded to the male parent, through part or all of her children's lifetime.

Any discussion of the sex life of the unmarried immediately stresses the dissociation between parenthood and sex. Since marriage and parenthood are bound together in the great majority of cultures, parenthood is disallowed as a consequence of sex activity of the unmarried.

How far this dissociation may go is vividly dramatized in the marriage blanket of the Algonkin Indians, of whom it is reported that in order to legitimatize a child, even after years of marriage, the intercourse responsible for its birth must have taken place through a special blanket which was a tribal possession guarded by a priest. With due recognition, then, of the almost universal requirement of marriage as ensuring two-sex social responsibility for a child, and the resulting dissociation of parenthood and sex activity, as well as of marriage and sex activity, in the lives of the unmarried, we can turn to a consideration of the patterning of the sex behavior of the unmarried in different cultures.

The Manus tribe of the Admiralty Islands controls the sex behavior of the unmarried by a rigid puritanical code which extends to all the women who are under the tutelage of Manus ghosts. Child-betrothal with strict avoidance between the betrothed pair is enjoined until marriage. The marriage age is determined by economic considerations and may occur anywhere between puberty and twenty-one or twenty-three for the girl, between eighteen and twenty-five for the boy. In the interval between puberty and marriage, the society rigidly chaperons the girls and permits extra-community license for the boys. As long as the turbulent youth respect the chastity of the women of their community, they are permitted to carry off a woman of an enemy village and keep her captive as a group prostitute, the original captor receiving fees in her name. The women of the community hate the prostitute because she is sometimes resorted to by the married men also, and because she stands for sex, which they were reared to hate. As a result, it is unsafe to leave her in the village, and the men must take her on their fishing trips and even to war. In default of prostitution and sometimes in addition to it, semi-public homosexual play in the boys' houses and occasional pairing off of boys occurs. The ghostly guardians of community morals take no cognizance of homosexuality and the pairing off does not survive the highly institutionalized marriage arrangements.

Meanwhile, the girls grow up in isolation; after puberty even friendship with girl relatives is frowned upon, for a girl with a confidante is a girl likely to be led astray. The girls are taught to hide their menstrual periods from everyone and to look upon their coming marriage with shame, resignation and dread. Physical affection is given hardly any expression in Manus; women never play with children and people never touch each other casually, except in a rough fashion in the jesting relationship. The girls grow up with no experience of warmth or physical responsiveness. The marriage, which is finally consummated between a highly inhibited girl and a man whose only sex experience had been the violent rape of a helpless woman by a group of men, results in a home atmosphere admirably calculated to induce similar attitudes in the children. They grow up with a frigid mother and a father who turns for confidence to his sister, and for physical affection to his infant children, for whose devotion he successfully competes with his even more inhibited wife. The religious system, interpreted by female mediums, commonly lays illness, misfortune and death to some offense against the sex or property codes. Both sexes take refuge in an aggressive economic life, and the men daydream of a lost golden age when ghosts were not interested in sex and a man could seize and rape every woman he encountered.

The Manus' concept of sex, which dominates the lives of the married and the unmarried, is one which sees man as a crudely sexual animal, and his sexual desires as antithetical to the orderly acquisition and exchange of property, which is the ideal of the whole society. The one aim is to exile sexuality beyond the borders of the community; the chastity of the unmarried girl is preserved by the admission of the foreign prostitute. This solution is, of course, a frequent one in many societies which regard aggressive sexuality on the part of the male as inevitable as it is undesirable. The years of license which the youths enjoy, as merely tolerated and unindustrious roisterers on the edge of a sober, money-getting community, serve to accentuate the antisocial conception of sex and encourage a form of marriage of which the women say: "When there are two children and the father sleeps always on one side of the house with one, while the mother sleeps on the other side of the house with the other, that is the happiest marriage."

The Omaha Indians trained their male youth to an aggressive sexuality and vigilantly chaperoned their unmarried girls. An Omaha boy believed that a woman found alone was fair game; and the girls, reared to a helpless dependence upon others, had no idea how to defend themselves. They clung desperately to their chaperons until marriage, while the young men experimented in group assault on the occasional loose woman, who by deserting the marriage bond had made herself their helpless victim. Here again we find the association of a puritanical view of sex and rape.

These pictures may now be compared with that of the Dobu Islanders, where the social attitude is one of snickering acceptance of the tendency of the human animal to indulge in sex activity whenever it is given the opportunity. The Dobuans make no distinction between the relative sexuality of men and of women and no attempt to curb one more than the other. Promiscuity for the adolescent is the order for both sexes, provided the members of one's own hamlet with its half dozen households are respected. Young boys are thrust out of their parents' hut, where their sisters are allowed unostentatiously to receive their lovers, and forced to wander nightly until they find some girl who will let them in. Sex and shelter become synonymous. Any move towards preference for one girl beyond another is likely to end this roving period. The mother of the girl will decide that it is now time to legalize a relationship which seems to be becoming a fairly constant one, and the boy will awake some morning to find her sitting form blocking the doorway and the whole village gathered outside to stare at him and thus publicly brand him as engaged. Any sort of fidelity, any exercise of choice, is the trap by which cheerfully, if salaciously, promiscuous youths are lured into matrimony.

The course of matrimony itself, with a background of promiscuity and an overweening insistence on fidelity with an enormous display of jealousy, is far from untroubled. The continuous suspicion, quarreling and divorce prove how unsuccessful the Dobuans have been in making a smooth course of life by first giving free rein to sex indulgence and then suddenly and arbitrarily curbing it in a jealous and insistent monogamy.

The Samoans share with the Dobuans a period of promiscuity before marriage, but the context is entirely different. Where the Dobuans regard sex as a violent, highly attractive, but withal, shameful interest, the Samoans regard it as amusing and somewhat frivolous, appropriate for the young but hardly compatible with the graver interests of the mature. There is freedom before marriage, but not of the Dobuan sort where every boy is sent adventuring and so involves every girl. In Samoa the chosen adventures of the unmarried are given no institutional recognition. Marriage takes place between those of relatively the same social status and, except for those of very high rank, it is largely on the indirectly expressed initiative of the young people. Pregnancy is believed to be the result of long and continuous intercourse with one person, and monogamous intercourse is regarded as an earnest of choice. Marriages make no violent claims for fidelity and achieve a remarkably low frequency of divorced; adultery does not necessarily lead to divorce and is not regarded as very serious.

Samoan society works very smoothly as it is based on the general assumption that sex is play, permissible in all hetero- and homo-sexual expression with any sort of variation as an artistic addition, and that older people have more serious occupations than the seeking of extramarital sex adventure. The occasional widower or widow has a series of adventures before a second marriage and is curbed only by the Samoan sense that affairs between people of very discrepant age are repellent. Furthermore, the whole emphasis of the period of promiscuity has been upon virtuosity of sex technique rather than upon personality. The Samoan child comes not from the narrow, jealously guarded walls of the Dobuan household, but from the wide, casual relationships of a household of some fifteen or twenty people, towards whom his attitude is one of generalized affection. In contrast to Manus, where sex is regarded as an ever-present moral problem; and to Dobu, where it is an ever-present emotional problem, with its special trappings of suspicion, jealousy and sometimes cases of passionate personal devotion; Samoa dissociates the whole matter of sex from any considerations of personality. Jealousy, special devotion, an excess of feeling are bad form. Anger is aroused only against those who do not keep the rules, who set a tryst which they do not keep.

Sex is a game, played according to one's age and rank; only the *taupou,* the daughter of the high chief, is supposed not to play at all, but to marry as a virgin. If she is not a virgin, she must have the courage to confess the fact, so that her virginity test may be gracefully faked. Sex is a skill in which one becomes adept and to which personality is felt to be as irrelevant as it might be to a consideration of table manners. Within the appropriate social class, one expects virtuosity from one's partner in the same way that one expects any other form of graceful social adequacy.

This Samoan attitude contrasts strongly with those already cited. The emphasis is laid not upon sex as a dangerous and powerful force, but as a pleasant aptitude of the human race at which it is suitable that those for whom it has no serious social consequences shall play and become proficient, with no fear that it will develop desires which cannot be easily channeled within a not-too-burdensome marriage bond.

The Arapesh, a mountain-dwelling group of Papuan people in New Guinea, have still another conception of sex. Like the Manus they practice child-betrothal, taking care that the girl of five or six years is betrothed to a youth some few years older than she. The small girl grows up living part of the time in her future husband's home and learning to include her fiancé, towards whom she need practice no avoidance, in the affection which she feels for all her male relatives. Warmth, easy affection, casual bodily contact are permitted in her relationship to all the males of her own and her husband's kin group. The young husband feeds his little wife; "he makes her body." Both boy and girl learn the overt attitudes towards sex which are expressed in every aspect of Arapesh ceremonial. Sex is good, and food and growth are good, but these goods are incompatible. The good life consists in balancing these incompatibles. The principal concern of young people is with growth; when the girl's breasts begin to develop, when the boy's pubic hair appears, certain foods must be taboo. Were the engaged couple to indulge in sex, their growth would be stunted. The only need for chaperonage, which the Arapesh recognize for those whose marriages are not yet consummated, is an informal supervision of these engaged pairs which continues until they are old enough so that sex will not hurt them. If the original estimate of the relative ages of the pair was wrong, if the girl grows too fast and outstrips the boy, then their parents fear that the two, who have known from childhood that they are destined for each other, may sleep together. This is the only sex activity of the unmarried against which the Arapesh feel it necessary to guard, premature response to a situation defined as sexual.

Of the insistent sexuality of man, which so many peoples take for granted, they know nothing; of the innate aggressiveness of the male they are equally ignorant. Sex is conceived of as a response to an appropriate situation. The mere presence of an unprotected woman is not regarded as a stimulus to sex activity and women go about alone and sleep unchaperoned in houses with male friends or relatives of their husbands. The lengths to which such an attitude may lead a people is well-illustrated in the taboo during lactation, when a man must sleep beside the mother of his child but have no intercourse with her. He may not even have intercourse with another wife if he has one, for his presence is necessary to make the child grow. It must be enclosed in the rounded circle of its parents' affection from which sex is temporarily and painlessly banished. With the lack of interest in sex, it is not surprising that homosexuality is practically unknown among the Arapesh. Sex is conceived of as play, play meaning in Arapesh any gentle, pleasantly toned activity. When a child is desired, however, sex activity is conceived as work. The Arapesh have pregnancy magic which they sometimes use, for it is said, "If people get tired of copulating, they can use pregnancy magic to help out."

The Ba Thonga of South Africa have constructed a different sort of dichotomy. There are two kinds of sex activity, the kind in which the completed procreative act is accomplished between husband and wife, and all other sorts, including surreptitious but permitted liaisons among the unmarried. The latter live in dormitories, one for each sex, just inside the gates of the kraal. The normal life of the kraal is symbolized by the first type of sex activity, and thus must always be rigorously taboo during any emergency period such as war, a death, or moving the village. These taboos apply with far less stringency to the casual sex activities of the unmarried, whose unsanctioned acts are not part of the stable order of the universe. South Africans regulate carefully the acceptance of individuals into full membership in society; the new born baby is not a person at all; the child up to puberty is not a member of the tribe; the unmarried youth is socially insignificant. The very permission to engage in sex during periods when responsible adults are conspicuously abstaining from it is only another way of stating the immature and irresponsible position of the unmarried. This point is of particular interest because it is often claimed that admission to sex activity is a necessary part of attaining adult status in society. According to the Ba Thonga attitude, it is not merely sex activity but responsible procreative sex activity which must be most rigorously interdicted during periods of stress, periods which are brought to a ceremonial end by each married couple, in order of seniority, practicing interrupted intercourse.

The problem of unmarried pregnancy is phrased among the Ba Thonga in terms of payment of wife indemnity. Children belong to their mother's group unless their father has paid for them. If a girl becomes pregnant and her lover wishes to marry her, he goes to her parents and says: "I have killed to eat," and pays the bride price. In this society paternity is a matter of payment and the whole emphasis is upon buying the child.

It is interesting to consider the wide variations of the definitions of marriage as a highly responsible state. This is best illustrated in the island of Mentawei, where so heavy are the ceremonial duties of a married man, and so rigorous the taboos on his economic activity, that the only men who can afford to marry are those who have adolescent sons old enough to assume part of the routine economic burden of the household. Until such time as this, men meet their unacknowledged wives secretly in the bush; children are adopted, as they are born, by their maternal grandfathers and supported by the labors of their maternal uncles; when they are partly grown, the husband marries his wife, adopts his children and sets up as a married man.

The Kiwai Papuans, who live in huge communal houses in the yielding sago swamps at the mouth of the Fly River in New Guinea, have a phrasing of sex which stands in odd contrast to that of the Ba Thonga and also to our own. Where the Ba Thonga celebrate every unusual event by continence, followed by ceremonial intercourse between pairs of husbands and wives, the Kiwai mark great occasions, such as building a new communal house, by mass promiscuity, in which the aim of the ceremony is to collect great quantities of sexual secretions to be used in subsequent rites to increase plants and people. To the Kiwai, sex is horribly dangerous and exceedingly powerful, but this great power is lodged not in the phallus but in the vulva, which, besides being the source of all magic and sorcery, is also compared to an open grave. Yet from this source man must derive all his success, as well as the forces of fear which may destroy him.

Against this background of dread female potency, parents take special precautions to prepare their sons for success in love. The parents contribute sexual secretions to make the boy love charms, they coach and ornament him so that he will win some girl's heart. The only magic ever exercised on behalf of a daughter is negative, inimical magic to upset the love affairs of other people's daughters. While the girls are all initiated into sex at the great festivals of purposive promiscuity, the boys must be theoretically chaste until marriage. All through life, the magical sexual potency of his wife is a man's greatest dependence, and should it not be exercised in his favor, he will not only not prosper but will come to grief. Among the Kiwai the male shares only slightly, and, as it were, by association, in this potency of the woman. Yet despite these theories, the Kiwais maintain a courtship pattern in which the boy must take the initiative, which insures that few boys are actually virgins at marriage.

It is against such a background as this, one which might be endlessly elaborated by examples from many other and different primitive societies, that the sexual activity of the unmarried in different primitive communities must be understood, as well as in terms of the more familiar institutional context of bride price, arranged marriage, property rights of the husband, and so on. It is of more far-reaching consequence whether or not man is viewed as a spontaneously sexual animal, than whether actual sex activity is interdicted for any special age or sex group in the community. If the "sex life of the unmarried adult" is interpreted in its widest sense, it means not presence or absence of overt activity but the whole view of sex and the permitted social expression of this view among those who are not assuming any responsibility for the begetting and rearing of children. Two very critical factors, therefore, are the conception of youth's place in society, and the conception of man's sexual nature. In Ba Thonga the sex activity of the young is a part of their unimportance; the Arapesh sanction against early sex activity is the preciousness of growth for the important young; in Kiwai the boys must be protected and carefully prepared for a life which girls may enter lustily and publicly.

Each one of these societies has selected one of the possible attitudes towards sex and has elaborated it. Whether the life of the unmarried is one of compulsory sex indulgence as in Dobu; compulsory abstinence for girls as in Manus; voluntary and unstressed abstinence for both sexes as in Arapesh or optional indulgence as in Samoa, depends upon these basic cultural sets. It is a frightening thing to be a girl among the Omaha Indians, brought up to believe that a man will attack any girl he finds alone; it is an equally frightening thing to be a boy among the Kiwai.

Considerations such as these demonstrate how naïve are the discussions which consider sex freedom for the unmarried in terms of the amount of restriction upon sex activity. The Arapesh youth grows up thinking very little about the subject; the Dobuans are thrust into sex activity whether they will or not. The problem of freedom for the majority of youth in any culture, excepting now those deviating temperaments to whom the standardized solutions of some other society would have been far more congenial, is primarily one of the degree of consistency in the sex concepts and the institutionalized attitudes of the group. Fidelity in marriage is far easier for an Arapesh, whose attention has never been centered upon sex as a continuous and urgent need, than it is for a Dobuan who has spent years in developing a self-conscious connoisseurship of the subject. Where both sexes are regarded as inherently, spontaneously, aggressively sexual from the time of puberty, society's insistence upon virginity at marriage or upon continence for the unmarried, results in coercion of almost every individual brought up in that society. This coercion may be external, as with chaperonage of Omaha girls. It may be a matter of individual repression, as among the Manus youth who must respect their own women for fear of ghostly punishment. Manus men, taken to other islands away from their watchful ghosts, lose all restraint. But coercion may be exercised in the opposite way. If sex is regarded as dread and dangerous for one or both sexes—as it is believed to be for boys in Kiwai—and the society then elaborates premarital courtship institutions involving the need for sex activity, conflict may again result between the fear of sex and the social insistence upon it.

The variety of ways in which different primitive groups solve this problem may be regarded from theoretically different points of view. We may say that the sexual constitution is similar in kind in all human beings, varying quantitatively but not qualitatively, and that the extraordinary differences in expression or repression which are found in the institutionalized attitudes of different peoples is simply one more comment upon the astounding adaptability of the human animal, which can learn to live in one society under conditions of promiscuity, and in another under conditions of rigorous monogamy or with long periods of sexual abstinence. It may be further assumed that any one of these diverse patternings of sexual behavior is the normal—the type of behavior which is most congenial to the requirements of man as an organism. This is the usual point of view taken by students of sex. A norm is recognized and a series of pathological, that is, statistically unusual deviations from the norm, are enumerated. (The treatment of this subject may vary from the assumption of many modern sexologists that climaxes are normal for all women and that any method of reaching a climax is therefore to be defined as normal, or the contrasting assumption that intercourse is the only normal manifestation of sex, with or without climax, and, then, any variant of sexual behavior is abnormal.) In any society where the traditional behavior is that which has been catalogued on the basis of our standards, as perverse, arrested development, undersexed, inverted, and so forth, these facts are airily reassimilated to our preconceived ideas of the norm, and the society is classified as infantile, sadistic, decadent, and so on, depending upon which set of values is being invoked.

The point of view I have presented is in definite contrast to such an attitude. Primitive material has been used, not to prove a set of *a priori* theories of the normal, based upon a cursory examination of a selected series defined as statistically normal within our society, but as raw material, evidence upon the sexual capacities of man. A consideration of this evidence suggests that the sexual tendencies in man lack in great measure the degree of specificity of patterned response characteristic of animals. Therefore, when a whole culture emphasizes a consistent attitude towards such a phenomenon as sex, it is suggested that this attitude towards sex is particularly congenial to and normal for certain human temperaments, and that it is not merely a curious aberration of the development of society. Whatever the pattern—be it rape or twelve-year periods of continence as preludes to an important religious festival; youthful romantic trysts or the death-punishment of unchastity in the unmarried; male aggressiveness and female responsiveness, female aggressiveness and male responsiveness; foreplay which is gentle and discriminating or foreplay which is a battle royal with blood-letting; intercourse in the sight of the whole camp or an excess of shyness which makes the husband visit his wife only in the dead of night—each and every one of these contrasting and uncomparable attitudes serves most perfectly the sexual constitution of some members of the human race. No sexual adjustment which has become an articulated part of the cultural pattern of any society can be branded as infantile, or immature or perverted, for our very conceptions of normality themselves are based upon no more accurate standards than the ability to adjust adequately to a culture pattern and to reproduce and rear another generation who will do the same.

In conclusion, almost all human societies insist upon the association between dual parentage and child rearing, and those cases where this requirement has been modified so as to exclude the father, either in terms of the mother's independence, as in Sparta, or only to replace him by a maternal grandfather or maternal uncle, are special developments of the much more widespread pattern which places the responsibility of parenthood upon a mated pair. Beyond this simple ground plan which all human societies honor, most of them in the observance and the remainder in the breach, there is the widest divergence in the social patterning of the sex life of the unmarried. The patterning in any society is a function of the social concept of the status of the young and of the importance and insistency of sex. Where sex is important and youth unimportant, one picture results, and another where sex and youth are both unimportant and so by definition suited to each other, as in Samoa.

Whatever its conceptions of the inherent immediacy of the sexual drive of man, each society succeeds in molding to its canons most of those born within it. And as there is no one type of sex behavior which is a constant for the human race, so there is no one sexual rôle for the young; but their attitudes toward sex, their use of their newly acquired physical maturity, the problems which confront them in adjusting to it, are a function of the concept of sex which their culture has institutionalized.

Minimum of difficulty obtains when there is harmony

between the theories of youthful sexuality and the institutionalized youthful behavior. Thus, conflict may be avoided by defining sexuality as a response to a situation rather than as a demand which the organism makes on an individual to initiate a situation, as in Arapesh, or by defining it as a spontaneous urge and then permitting its gratification as in Dobu. Other societies, like Manus and Omaha, attempt a more difficult task; they define youth as spontaneously sexual and then seek to curb that sexuality. It is possible for a culture to make its conceptions and its institutions consistent one with another, or to elaborate institutions the goal of which is to curb and limit human nature as that society has defined and fostered it. There is no evidence at present available from primitive society to suggest that either the prohibition or the permission of sex activity to the young is necessarily more congenial to the sexual nature of mankind. Only after society has selected some one of the many variations of human sexuality, some one of the widely differing rates of maturity, and has based upon these conceptions its attitudes toward the sexuality of youth, does the rôle which it institutionally allots to youth become more or less difficult for those who grow up within its limits.

Whatever the formulated youthful attitude toward sex, there always will be individuals to whom it will be uncongenial. The aggressively sexed boy or girl is a misfit in Arapesh. The Dobuan boy who wearies of the nightly amorous round can find a temporary refuge from it only if there happens to be a widower's house in which he can sleep. The Samoan girl who falls in love with her first lover and cannot adjust to a more transitory flexibility in her choices, is unhappy and frustrated. No society will be without a few deviants whose temperament is too aberrant to be redirected, even within the iron grip of a simple homogeneous culture. But whether the period between physical maturity and marriage is one of conflict for the individual or for the whole age group, it varies from society to society and is not correlated with the presence or absence of overt sex expression.

# BIOLOGY

Now all organisms find—as human beings find and some loudly proclaim—that the business of reproduction interferes with their careers. The two things interact, intertwine, modify each other. . . . The number and variety of systems arising from the interaction of reproduction with the pursuit of life career are so great as to defy enumeration.—H. S. JENNINGS

## THE BIOLOGY OF SEX AND THE UNMARRIED ADULT

*N. W. Ingalls, M.D.*

ASSOCIATE PROFESSOR OF ANATOMY,

SCHOOL OF MEDICINE,

WESTERN RESERVE UNIVERSITY

OUT OF the vast and varied heritage which man's less exalted ancestors have passed on to him, few if any elements have left such widespread and indelible impressions as those concerned with sex and reproduction. Little wonder, then, that with such beginnings and rooted so deeply in a purely biological animal soil, man's manifold activities and his myriad institutions and conventions should, from their very inception, have been so molded and colored by sexual influences; or that his entire history, his literature and art, as well as his religion, should so insistently remind us that sex and life are one and inseparable.

Life, or living material, is so constituted that, to maintain itself, it must reproduce or propagate; a stagnant static life is doomed; only as life begets life is it assured of a continuance. Hence, in the very beginning, the absolute necessity of reproduction asserts itself and all other processes become subservient to it. Its prime importance may be judged from the varied and elaborate means which nature has provided for its accomplishment, as well as by the tenacity with which it is preserved when almost everything else has been sacrificed.

At first, reproduction was simply the breaking up of a larger, older mass into smaller parts which grew in size and again repeated the process, but later more specialized portions were given off by the parent forms and these, uniting with each other, two and two, gave rise to a new individual. It was when these uniting or conjugating cells began to differ from each other that we had the beginning of Sex. Sex then, is a means or method; it is not primary and is never an end. The two cells just noted are the germ cells, or sex cells. The larger, contributing more building material for the future individual, is the ovum or egg; while the smaller, initiating development in the egg but having an equal hereditary value, is the sperm cell, or spermatozoon.

Correlated with these differences in the sex cells and due to the same factors, there are also differences in the adult parent forms which distinguish them as male or female. Most conspicuous here are the primary sex characters, the sexual organs. These have to do with the formation of sex cells within the sex glands or gonads, testicle and ovary; they also provide the means, copulatory organs, for the union of the male and female elements, fertilization; and provision, in the female, for extended development before birth.

In addition to these essential and more primitive features there may be a host of other differences, secondary sex characters. These are less directly concerned with reproduction, but are more ancillary and adaptive in nature, since they contribute in various ways to the assurance of normal reproductive function. As differences in size and strength, body build and general appearance, in color and ornamentation or in the possession of special features, they are too familiar to call for further notice. But all this sexual *accoutrement* would be vain and idle were not, at the same time, adequate provision made for drawing or driving the sexes together, and the underlying, biologic need for reproduction is a measure of the intensity and the imperiousness of that drive. It is here, in external adjustments or mutual relations in sexual behavior, that the senses and the nervous system, the feelings and the mind, become irrevocably woven into the picture, and this union of sex and sense has been fraught with inevitable and immeasurable consequences for mankind.

Whatever his mental caliber or capacity, man still sees or feels the world with the same old sense organs; the gradual ascendancy of brain over brawn has left his senses and feelings largely unchanged, his primitive passions for the most part unabated; and one may expect to find in his conduct and proclivities many things which are easier to explain than to justify.

Although the chief concern in nature, reproduction can be assured only by the preliminary growth and the attainment of proper maturity in the parent organism. It is natural, therefore, that those influences which preside over growth and differentiation should also be important in bringing about normal sexual development.

While the primary sex characters have always been present, they remain relatively immature and quiescent for a considerable period during infancy and childhood. In the second decade, however, by twelve to fourteen years, the general body development has progressed sufficiently so that the growth factors now become more specific and begin to exert their influence upon the sex organs. Most important here is the hypophysis, or pituitary gland, at the base of the brain; under its stimulation the gonads increase rapidly in size and inaugurate their own functional activity. In response to gonadal secretion, sex hormones or endocrines, the sexual organs now resume their development, increase in size and differentiate still further until their adult or functional condition is attained. This comparatively sudden onset of sexual development marks the time of puberty. More striking and more sharply defined in the female, ovarian function shows itself in the establishment of menstruation; while the signs of testicular activity are less conspicuous and often first appear at a somewhat later date.

Further evidences of gonadal influences are seen in the postpubertal years during adolescence, in the gradual development of secondary sexual characters and the full flowering of the adult form. One may contrast the greater strength and stature, the broader shoulders, more rugged build, the deeper voice and the more abundant hair on the face and body in the male, with the smaller and more rounded outlines of the female, her characteristic breasts, broader hips and softer voice, and her fairer, smoother skin with a more generous supply of underlying, relieving fat.

Some of these feminine features are obviously concerned in reproduction, as the breasts and pelvic proportions, but all of them, and others might be added, appeal alike to the senses and to the fancy. The strength and insistence of that appeal may be seen in the extent to which the secondary sexual characters of the female appear in art and literature at every turn.

Toward the close of the second decade adolescence is giving way to maturity; the body, in a sense, is finished; growth has ceased; physical form and function are at or near their peak. Biologically, maturity is full reproductive capacity in a body properly and adequately adjusted thereto. That this is the chief criterion is evidenced by the tendency of the sex hormones to slow up or arrest growth, to put an end to further changes or advances except as they concern reproduction.

In man, however, these relatively simple conditions have been altered; he develops and matures more slowly than any other animal. Infancy and childhood extend into the second decade, more than the whole life span of many other forms; and after puberty he faces a very protracted adolescence. Even his next of kin, the Anthropoids, have a much shorter childhood and almost no adolescent period. This extreme retardation, which seems to be correlated in some way with man's special cerebral development, is most in evidence after puberty. In other words, reproductive ability may appear at the end of childhood, as in animals generally, but full bodily maturity is still several years in the future. Even after this belated maturity, man lives far longer than most animals, and while he may pass his physical prime in the forties, if not earlier, sexual ability may remain unimpaired for many years; or, like intellectual capacity, it may persist to a green old age, although in the female, the menopause, around the forty-fifth year, marks the end of the reproductive phase of life.

Not only do the sex endocrines bring about the striking changes characteristic of puberty, and in addition call forth and control a variety of secondary sexual features, but they are also responsible for the active carrying out of reproductive function since they determine the behavior of the animal, the relation of the sexes to each other. Under their influence the immature, largely sexless, child gradually begins to see things in a new light and sex appears in others as it becomes dominant in himself. The natural playfulness and exuberance of spirit, which are at first free and untroubled and make no distinctions as to sex, become more and more tempered and colored by vague inner feelings which indicate and insist that there are two quite different kinds of people.

This sensing of the idea and significance of another, opposite sex—for it is a feeling, deep and primitive, rather than any definite thinking—pervades more and more the attitudes and activities of the adolescent. There is a greater emotional sensitivity, a shyness and self-consciousness which betray the presence of disturbing elements, indefinite longings and desires in which sex becomes increasingly apparent, a clearer consciousness of sexual differences and their implications, with a stronger, subtler attraction and response, until almost imperceptibly the natural, sexless play of childhood leads on to more definite and more intimate relations. This normal sexual drive and the impulses to meet and satisfy it, this perfectly natural attraction of the sexes for each other, is simply an expression of nature's insistent demand that the race shall not die out, and this demand she imposes upon all her children. If, in the case of man, these primitive passions have borne other than their natural fruit, if they have been distorted and debased in countless ways and been forced to pander to the individual instead of serving the race; or if, on the other hand, they have been sublimed and transfigured almost beyond recognition; we still have before us only the protean manifestations of one primeval urge, further evidences of its intensity and power.

In the great majority of cases development runs its appointed course, but in man, perhaps more often than in other animals, it may be disturbed or retarded or assume unnatural forms. It can hardly be said that civilized man lives and matures in especially favorable, really natural surroundings, and his long childhood and adolescence only increase the opportunities for unfavorable or abnormal conditions to exert their influence. Variations in the nature or intensity of endocrine influences, in conjunction with inherited differences in bodily constitution, are responsible for the endless variety in sex and its manifestations, running the whole gamut from complete masculinity to perfect femininity, with a most unnatural array of mixed and neutral forms in between. As a rule, the more serious disturbances are deficiencies in development; arrested development of the sex organs, poorly defined secondary characters, with a corresponding lack in normal sexual tastes, as well as often in social inclinations. Often these poorly sexed individuals adopt the clothing, manners and employment of the "opposite" sex and not infrequently there are decided homosexual tendencies. At times, however, sexing appears to involve the mind rather than the body; there is a sort of psychic hermaphroditism or inversion, a deep-seated psycho-biological imbalance which also manifests itself in homosexual and allied practices.

In man, as in many other animals, homosexuality may be simply a case of substitution, a mere *faute de mieux*. Often it is to be looked upon as a retardation in sex development, in that the normal heterosexual stage is never reached, but in man only does it sink to the level of a confirmed perversity. On the other hand, normal sex impulses and attitudes may be found where the sex organs are so defective or malformed that their natural functions are either seriously impaired or even rendered quite impossible. While exceptional, these cases are perhaps more amenable to treatment than those in which the trouble is in mind rather than in body. Naturally, most of these aberrant cases, particularly those which deviate most widely from the normal state, help swell the ranks of the unmarried. Here also, outside the fold, may be found a few whose secondary characters leave too much to be desired; but sex is not always very critical and marriage does not demand concrete perfection.

As man's body, both in structure and function, shows his descent from non-human ancestors, so his sexual peculiarities and behavior are to be derived from similar sources. As his human characteristics, his erect posture, his hands and his brain, have made him largely independent of his surroundings, so also his sexual life has been freed from its earlier restrictions and limitations.

The most characteristic feature of the reproductive function among animals is its periodicity, alternate and recurring periods of activity and quiescence, the sexual or œstrus cycles. This rhythmic ebb and flow is the expression of a corresponding rise and fall in the sex hormones, conditioned for the most part by such environmental factors, seasonal, climatic, and so forth, as are important for the birth and survival of the young. In its most primitive and most pronounced form, there is a short period during which ova and spermatozoa, as well as sex hormones, are formed. The latter bring about typical changes in behavior; the mutual interest and attraction of the sexes, the acceptance of the male by the female, all those features which characterize the breeding or mating season, "heat" or œstrus, the period of desire. With the sexual functions in abeyance, sex also drops out of the picture and during the intervals between reproductive activities the animal is practically sexless in behavior. In view of the rôle of the mother in the development, birth and subsequent care of the young, it is natural that this rigid reproductive program should apply particularly to the female, and in the female of the species this reproductive sexual rhythm has never been entirely abolished.

Further advances toward reproductive independence are encountered in a variety of forms, among them most domesticated animals and many which live in tropical climates. There, the adult male may be quite freed from any seasonal or periodic sexuality; his sex endocrines are continually active, and therefore germ cells are being formed constantly, he is always sexually excitable and in readiness for sexual relations. Indeed, it may not even require the natural stimulation of the female in heat to release a train of associations leading up to intercourse or to attempts or substitutes for it. In the female, however, we still find the same periodic changes as before, but perhaps at more frequent intervals. Only at certain times and for a brief period do the ovaries produce ripe ova and pour out their internal secretion. Under the stimulation of these secretions, changes are brought about in the genitalia preparatory to the reception and nourishment of the fertilized ovum and at the same time the outward phenomena of heat or œstrus become evident. Rarely, except when moved by ovarian hormones and when a ripe ovum awaits fertilization, will the female accept the advances of the male or permit or coöperate in sexual relations. During the longer or shorter intervals when ovarian function is dormant and pregnancy impossible she is practically sexless and as a rule quite devoid of sex appeal.

What may be looked upon as the last stage in sexual development, the almost complete liberation of reproductive function from the vicissitudes and exigencies of external conditions, is seen in the higher Primates and more especially in Man. The advances to be noted here apply particularly to the female, since the male has long since reached this stage. There is still the same periodic ovarian activity but it is rather more diffuse, its ups and downs are less accentuated, it is more sustained and perhaps less intense. These rhythmic changes make up the menstrual cycle of the Anthropoids and Man, corresponding with the œstrus cycle in lower forms. Each lunar month, on the average, except during pregnancy, the mature female makes all the necessary preparations for conception; an ovum is matured and set free and the uterus is prepared to receive and care for it.

What distinguishes the female in these cases then is not any departure from the time-honored program of periodic ovarian influence, since all of this is still substantially the same and still serves its original purpose. What has happened is that this periodicity is now largely confined to the body, i.e., the necessary arrangements looking toward pregnancy; while the corresponding periodic œstrus, with its striking behavioral manifestations, has almost vanished. The female, in her conduct and inclinations, has become more like the male; mating may occur at any time and no specific physiological stimulus is necessary; but remnants of the older rhythm may still be recognized in those fluctuations, increases in sexual appetite which occur around the menstrual period, not always conspicuous but typically periodic. The most significant feature of this anthropoid stage is to be found in the absence of any definite, sharply circumscribed œstral period. The brief, acute, but infrequent, upheavals of the typical œstrus have been replaced by a somewhat milder but more continual desire; sex has become a more constant, less intermittent influence in the animal's life, more varied and more personal in its expression, less a blind racial drive.

It is here that we shall find the beginnings of, and the explanation for, much of man's sexual behavior. While not unknown in lower species, the tendency to form sexual partnerships is much better developed in the Anthropoids, where a number of females may be associated with a single male in the formation of a simple social group or "harem," and a number of these harems may be found together. Within these groups the mutual attachments of male and female are strongest when ovarian activity is at its height during what remains of œstrus, at which periods also the dominance of the male is most in evidence and copulation is most frequent. Outside this circle may be found the immature young and those males to whom no females have attached themselves.

Associated, it would seem, with the slowly increasing mental capacity, there are a number of sexual features which become more conspicuous and more important as we approach human conditions. One of the results of the close sexual association just noted is a certain fatigue or indifference to accustomed stimuli, whereas a change in stimulation, in the form of another female, may bring out in full strength all of the natural responses. This principle of fatigue has a very general application to the senses and the brain, but in the realm of sex it has wrought untold havoc. It might be looked upon as the biological reason, or excuse, for some degree of promiscuity or variety. As specific œstral reproductive stimuli become progressively less important in releasing or initiating sexual responses, we may be prepared to find that sexual activities and reproduction will become more widely separated and that new outlets for old instincts will appear.

Although sporadic cases occur in lower animals, unnatural methods of sexual gratification are not uncommon among the Anthropoids; this holds particularly for the males, especially such as have no attendant females. Autosexuality or autoerotism and homosexuality are most in evidence here, but zoöphilia and even suggestions of sadism may be encountered. Too much significance need not be ascribed to these conditions; most of them are but the erratic expressions of inner promptings, inevitable results, perhaps, of the shifting of sexual control from the endocrines to the nervous system. They are incidents in the animal's life, substitutes for other things, and they disappear, as a rule, when normal heterosexual relations become established.

It is well to remember, when we attempt to explain or to judge man's sexual conduct, that he parted company with his anthropoid cousins at least a million years ago. He took with him his sexual freedom, and a decided inclination to restrict his attentions to certain females, but there followed him, like his shadow, a temptation for variety, for a change in his sexual fare. For a million years his life has revolved around these old, deeply ingrained habits; out of them have grown most of his social customs and conventions. After all this time they are still substantially unaltered, and to them he has contributed little really new.

In the meantime, important changes have taken place in his body; he has become fully erect, able to move around with ease and speed and use his hands to a greater advantage, but above all his mental capacity has been enormously enhanced. The most significant feature here would appear to be that, as a result of these innovations and of certain changes in pelvic adjustments, the male is now, for the first time, able to impose, or inflict, his will upon the female. Hitherto the consent and coöperation of the female had been necessary for intercourse; up to this time the female had held the balance of power in sexual affairs; and this passing of control to the male has left a deep and indelible impression upon the habits and customs of the whole human family.

In her new rôle the female may accept this control, resist or avoid it as best she may, or finally turn it to her own profit or advantage.

Perhaps the only Primate character which has shown any improvement or elevation in status during human development is man's more pronounced tendency to longer sexual association with a few or a smaller number of females. To what extent, however, social rather than strictly biological influences may have been at work, must raise a question. There is no direct information which might enable us to bridge the gap between what appears to have been man's original state and present-day conditions. We have no knowledge of any races or tribes which are not very far removed, in time at least, from anything even approaching really primitive conditions. It would appear that man has followed his old anthropoid habit, but slowly decreasing the size of his "harem," until somehow, not very long ago, perhaps, there gradually emerged more definite and more tangible relations out of which "marriage" finally evolved.

The origin of marriage is still a much disputed question. Has man always been essentially monogamous or has he come up from a state often designated as promiscuity? The available evidence points to the latter. As an animal, in his sexual make-up, and in his beginnings as far as we can reconstruct them, he is anything but monogamous; and one would have great difficulty in explaining, biologically, such a sudden change of heart, the transition from the harem to a single wife. On the other hand, a great many of his customs and regulations, among them marriage itself, seem to be aimed directly at his inveterate inclination for a change, for some measure of variety; they are checks or restrictions which would lose most if not all of their significance if the tendency to their infraction had not always been present.

Here, also, belong the many and varied measures which have been devised to protect the female against the male. If, in the beginning, man was strictly monogamous, then indeed there has been a "fall," but if, as seems much more probable, he was once given to what might be looked upon as a mild, but not unregulated, promiscuity, then we must credit him with some improvement. Whatever may have been its origin, marriage is a social and not a biological institution; it is a relatively late outgrowth of older sexual habits, and its presence or absence or the particular form it may assume are of little if any biological significance.

While man's sexual status has changed but little during his long development, and the alterations in his body have been minor, although very important, his mental faculties and his intellectual equipment have been amazingly refined and increased. But this plastic, highly impressionable mind, from its first dull glimmerings has been fairly steeped in the traditions of sex and there is little reason to be surprised that ever since it has been busied with this age-old theme. Doubtless this greater mental capacity has brought with it a keener appreciation and a deeper and more vivid enjoyment of sex and all its various possibilities. Not that the primary sense impressions have been altered particularly, but rather that they are more extensive and more variegated, distilled, as it were, in the alembic of the mind, into new colors and new intensities.

None of the senses has escaped the thrall of sex; all of them contribute to the finished picture. Even among the Anthropoids, the play of childhood is tinged with erotic elements; movements, attitudes and reactions arise which later pass over unaltered into specific sexual acts. What is substantially the same thing, sexual play, has undergone an enormously varied development in man; all the way from the simplest diversions and amusements in which sex is often unthought of, through the whole gamut of the senses and appetites, to the more concrete and tangible preliminaries of actual consummation. Unlike the animal, man can choose and find both interest and satisfaction at any and all of these levels; he may read between the lines, if that suits his purpose, and give his fancy full swing, or he can himself supply or simulate those elements which choice, convention or circumstances may deny him. Here, in the mutual interrelations of body and mind, lie the foundations, the biology of eroticism in its widest sense. With sharpened senses and a better brain, man is well prepared to exploit all the possibilities of sex, and although he may have added little essentially new to his Primate repertoire, he has contributed very conspicuously to the increasing divorcement of sex and procreation.

Sex and its gratification have become increasingly an end rather than a means. A subtle, sensuous attraction replaces the older biologic drive; there is a waxing of more personal and more pleasurable motives as the simpler and more straightforward earlier instincts are on the wane. With his greater intellectual and imaginative powers the picture of sex and the significance of sexual characters become vastly more varied and colorful. Man senses sexual features and sees erotic elements where other animals find nothing; he can magnify or idealize whatever may strike his fancy, and his great gift of association and suggestion paves the way for all manner of substitutions, erotic symbolism or cults and fetishes without end.

It is natural, or inevitable, that man's sexual conduct, as well as his other dealings with his fellows, should be complicated by just those features which set him apart from and above all other living forms; these include his capacity for feeling and enjoyment, for thought and for action, and his ability and ingenuity in molding things to suit himself. Unfortunately, the development of intellectual power has been attended by no commensurate guarantees that it would be dispensed in the best interest of the individual, much less of the race. To man's strongly animal appetites there have been added not only a cunning mind but, also, a more pronounced individuality, a greater variability in his general make-up, an enhanced susceptibility to disturbing influences. A stronger propensity toward the formation of habits, either good or bad, has developed, and an increased likelihood of his being conditioned to many more or less artificial influences. His protracted childhood and adolescence, and even his longer life, afford greater opportunity for adverse or abnormal circumstances to twist or upset his delicately balanced feelings and emotions and divert them into unusual or unnatural channels.

Biologically, these considerations may carry little weight—they are the materials out of which have been fashioned man's social and moral relationships—but, when biology runs counter to convention, it is the latter which may be expected to show the more conspicuous signs of conflict. Biological impulses and compulsions are too old and too deep-seated to be materially altered by present institutions and regulations, nor need one fear that the biology of sex or the attainment of its natural ends, the continuance of the race, will be appreciably affected either by the conventions which hedge it round or by the aberrations with which it may be encumbered.

Marriage and non-marriage, like the moral and the immoral, are not biological concepts, although all of them have sprung from natural sources; the former revolving around the relations of the sexes, the latter involving the mutual relations of individuals. Both matrimony and ethics are somewhat elastic and uncertain in their outlines; each has had to contend with the older animal nature, in the one case with sex, in the other with self; and neither has been entirely successful. Both have erected barriers around their particular preserves and have hurled anathemas at all dissenters. Each has invoked the law and the prophets to the end that a better order might prevail, but neither has changed materially the deep undercurrents of an older dispensation, the ceaseless ebb and flow of natural desires and appetites. One cannot quarrel with nature nor impugn her purposes if she is reluctant to conform to rules and regulations which neither interest nor concern her. If the development of the mind has brought with it confusing and discordant elements, then the mind alone can solve these problems.

The practical universality of marriage is sufficient evidence of the abiding influence of sex in the social order, but the fact that sexual relations and marriage have never been exactly equivalent or coextensive furnishes a fair measure of the relative strengths of the older natural drives and the newer artificial restrictions. Sporadic attempts to eliminate all sexual expression by voluntary or imposed celibacy or continence merely illustrate the extent to which the mind may dominate the body. Entirely practicable for some people, these conditions would be quite intolerable for others, but there is little if anything to indicate that such abstention from natural sexual activity entails any material consequences for the individual or for the race as a whole. The same may be said of a multitude of other practices and procedures, including even downright perversions; whether innocent varieties of sexual play or more intimate relations; whether conforming to or in defiance of accepted conventions; whether favorable to or designed rather to prevent conception. None of them possess any special biological significance.

At the biological animal level, sex is a racial affair rather than a personal attribute; it is for the next generation, not for the present one, and, insofar as its primary reproductive purpose is adequately fulfilled, other forms or degrees of sexual expression would appear to be of little moment. Since, at this level, sex does not serve the individual (indeed it is absent often enough), it can hardly be argued that the failure to employ its offices or make use of it in any way need be visited by any particular penalties beyond the obvious extinction of the line.

Above this level, however, when we leave the body and consider instead the mind and the usual social standards, the problems of sex become much more involved. We meet here a famous triangle, but in a somewhat different, more general, form—a basic sexual drive, but of greatly varying intensity and quality; and a fairly simple system intended for its direction and control; while the third part, the most important and the least predictable, the most variable and the least tangible, is represented by the individual personality. Out of the interrelations of these elements may come honor and happiness, or shipwreck between the Scylla of sex and the Charybdis of convention. From the straight and narrow way laid out by nature in the very beginning, man has wandered far and wide. No other animal has, or could have, descended into such sloughs of perversity and unnatural excesses, but neither could any other living form have reached such heights or have so transcended its own humble origin. The great highway of sex, stretching backward almost to the very dawn of life, has many byways; not a few of these well-trodden paths were there when man appeared, others of his own devising have been added; some of them lead upward to higher and better things, others return again to lower levels. All of them bear witness to a common origin and a common power.

Without doubt, one of nature's most invaluable assets has been her ability to reach the same end in different ways. Over and over again throughout her long history older structures have taken on newer functions; she has shown an amazing fertility in remodeling and rearranging, in diverting older forces into newer channels and in utilizing what she has for what she needs. She has been preëminently successful in putting new wine into old bottles. The annals of mankind record no other like measure of success, for all too often the heady wine of power and lust has broken the frail vessels of law and order intended to contain it.

Perhaps biology contains the answers to its own questions, for from first to last it is little more than a recital of the adjustments of life to its surroundings—and all human problems fall within this category. Doubtless the incentives furnished by the primitive emotions are as strong as ever, but there appears to be no inherent reason why these older influences should not, at a higher level, be transmuted into newer and nobler activities in the same way and for the same reason that, at a lower level, older structural elements have been transformed into newer organs and better instruments. Both are merely phases in that perpetual and eternal adjustment which is life, albeit at different levels; and in the face of new conditions and changed surroundings, nature's invariable response has been to adapt what she already has and fit it to the new requirements. For man such a procedure or solution would appear all the more promising since he, unlike nature, can exercise some choice and control over his environment. If out of limbs, which at first could hardly drag the body out of the sea where it was born, nature has made wings to fly into the very face of the sun, surely man need not despair. While the story of mankind has not been altogether flattering, it nevertheless indicates very clearly that even sex may adapt itself to new conditions and use its energies in new expressions. As nature, in all her various manifestations, has never sacrificed anything really essential, so one need not fear that the power or purpose of sex will be infringed upon in any way if it appears in somewhat different rôles.

Although furnishing the basic patterns and possibilities for sexual behavior and providing the natural driving force, biology must leave most of the details to the discretion, or the desire, of the individual; having given man such a large measure of freedom, nature can no longer dictate all of his activities, but by the same token neither can she be blamed for all of his shortcomings. One of the more significant aspects of this sexual freedom, taken in conjunction with the personality behind it, is that man can seek and find sex expression and sexual satisfaction in a variety of forms outside of actual consummation. Without overstepping any biological precedents, sex may expand its energy and enthusiasm in social enjoyments and more sensuous contacts; or, refined and sublimated by the fire of circumstances or necessity, it may be devoted to more impersonal things. The measure of success in any particular case will be determined by the individual qualities involved, for what may be simple or even natural for some people may be quite out of the question for others. One need not expect that the rank and file of humanity will be satisfied with substitutions and still less with sublimations; and neither of these can be counted on for material aid in any social system.

Having set the stage and suggested the main outlines of the plot, nature has left it to each actor to supply his own particular lines. The play goes on as it has from time immemorial. As heretofore, some of the acts may not conform to current usage or convention and here and there a scene may be quite without the pale. While the theme remains much the same, the players come and go, each cast in his own peculiar rôle; some in the rags of the gutter, others in the trappings of nobility; some wear the harness of war and strife, while others are clothed in the vestments of religion; each in his own way proclaims the power of Sex—all acknowledge her allegiance.

# PSYCHOLOGY

. . . since habits involve the support of environing conditions, a society or some specific group of fellow-men is always accessory before and after the fact. Some activity proceeds from man; then it sets up reactions in the surroundings. Others approve, disapprove, protest, encourage, share and resist. Even letting man alone is a definite response. Envy, admiration and imitation are complicities. Neutrality is non-existent.

—JOHN DEWEY

## SEX PSYCHOLOGY OF THE UNMARRIED ADULT

*Ernest R. Groves*

PROFESSOR OF SOCIOLOGY,

UNIVERSITY OF NORTH CAROLINA

IF BY ignoring a problem we could destroy it, there would be little sex life before marriage. Even yet, it is orthodox to consider sex a docile impulse that observes the social proprieties and makes appearance only when the man and the woman have crossed the barrier into matrimony. Any premarriage expression is unnatural, menacing, a behavior problem. We have gone so far in the recent past as to expect the boy and the girl to make the passage of puberty, with all its body changes, without becoming conscious of its sex meaning. The veil that taboo has spread over the sex life of the unmarried has been so thick that it has concealed the experience of all except those who have been considered problem persons. That society has ever been committed to such an imposture reveals more than anything else how large a problem sex before marriage has been.

Of late the curtain has been torn. The comfortable assumption, that sex can be kept quiescent until marriage invites it to come forth, is at an end. Instead, we find facing us some stubborn and uncomfortable facts once we permit the investigation that prejudice has so long blocked.

The evidences of the sex problems of the unmarried have ever been near the surface. Now that the myth of the non-sex career has been exploded, we are beginning to see why there is a problem and why it is so troublesome. Body maturity runs way ahead of marriage opportunity, so that normally the body is ready for adult sex experience years before men and women are ready for matrimony, according to the prevailing standards of culture. This is not all. Physical sex itself is discordant. As a pleasure-giving impulse, the adolescent sex changes come to maturity sooner than they do as a reproduction function. This division lifts the human sex life out of that of the animal by giving opportunity for psychic enlargement but, at the same time, it becomes an inevitable source of stress.

More trouble comes because those who are thrown into the pubescent upheaval have seldom been prepared for the ordeal forced upon them. Even now, when many parents are beginning to realize the trial of the adolescent, the great majority of children are given no inkling as to the meaning of what is happening to them, and they wrestle with forces that seem to have arisen in the night and without warning. Although sex is presented before the eyes of youth by the movies and other commercial enterprises and used as an exploiting motive, it is only in the rare family that any considerable effort is made to handle the sex problems of the growing child intelligently, frankly, and without any emotion or deception. It would not matter if there were some other way of getting the information and the attitudes which provide favorable passage through adolescence, but the failure of church and school is generally just as great as that of the parent.

For many older youths, particularly young women, trouble comes from another quarter, and this constitutes one of the most pressing of all the vexations of premarriage experience. There is no certainty in the vast majority of cases that the individual will finally pass out of the single life and enter upon marriage. However strong the individual's expectations, however optimistic the hope of finding a life-mate may be, there is always a lingering shadow of doubt, an uncertainty that cannot be pushed aside. It would be one thing for young women to struggle through the temporary testing if there were assurance of its ending in marriage, but only optimists having extraordinary recklessness or good fortune can feel sure that they will marry when they are ready, and only then if they are not too exacting in their choice.

As science pushes forward and gains in its conquest of knowledge of human experience, the significance of sex both before and after marriage constantly increases. We are amazed at the extent to which it is spread through the tissue of personality and the depth to which it is planted in the character. The secretions that pour forth from the testicles and ovaries have an essential part in the endocrine symphony and their contribution is far more complex than the sexual aspects of reproduction ever indicate. Recent discoveries relating to these chemical processes of the body are revolutionizing medical practice as did the investigations of Pasteur, and all of them emphasize the importance of the rôle of physiological sex for both the man and the woman.

Meanwhile, from a different source, comes another insistence that sex has a larger meaning for the human career than appears on the surface. Our increasing knowledge of this greater significance of sex we owe chiefly to the original explorations of Sigmund Freud and their stimulating effect upon both his disciples and his critics. The psychiatrist and the psychologist, divided though both of them are into groups that differ in their interpretation of sex, unite in affirming that it has a causal influence on human conduct beyond anything ever conceived in the past. Instead of it being, as was once supposed, only the licentious or the abnormal who bring sex into overt expression before marriage, we are forced to recognize the fact, staring at us from all directions, that from birth onward sex plays an active rôle continuously through life and never accepts expulsion. Not only is there never a time when sex is quiescent; it always refuses to be passive. The crossing, which in the past has been thought of as the time and method of bringing sex into activity, is a purely social boundary which the body does not recognize—an attempt at the regulation of sex for purposes that are larger than the impulses of the individual.

From this point of view, sex development is irregular, with personal differences of tension and with periods of special stress, but always it is a never-ending struggle for integration, not ended by marriage but given a different form. Within or without matrimony sex impulse craves satisfaction, a completeness, a fulfillment, and requires a discipline which makes it an epitome of human life itself. The tendency to elude the human grasp is one of the marked characteristics of our existence. Sex has this same everlasting groping, this quenchless craving, this restless turning to the future. At best, marriage can only soften the discord of conflicting motives and tone down the aggressiveness of adolescent expectation. Marriage, however, as the supremely intimate, complementary experience, leads away from this adolescent stress toward a maturity and a fellowship that mitigates all forms of struggle, whatever their origin.

We are too prone to dissociate the sex career of the individual and to think of it as chiefly an adjustment of one person to another in the fellowship of marriage. Only in narrow and deceptive terms can it be so conceived. We arbitrarily minimize the sex character of premarriage associations through motives similar to those that led our parents to ignore the existence of sex problems of children and adolescents.

A great part of the sex life of the unmarried is beneath the surface, and if it rises to consciousness it is in such form that the source from which the influences flow forth escapes attention. It is because of this concealment that there has been until of late the widespread notion that sex means little to the unmarried except when it becomes a conscious physical urge. On the contrary, we now know that traits that appear in the spinster or the bachelor, however distant they may seem from sex, are often the coming out of sexual reactions and conflicts that had their beginning as far back as infancy or early childhood. Even for those married and happily adjusted there is a large amount of psychic and physical incitements that are sexual in their origin but are not so interpreted by the persons whom they affect. Both in our changing moods and in our inconsistent emotions there are derivatives of sex.

There has been a disposition in the past to regard sex as essentially reproduction and to insist that its advent is at puberty. By squeezing sex into so narrow an interpretation a great part of its effect upon the unmarried was covered up. Even when the virgin has no thought of physical sex and no sublimating of it through a love-fixation, there are both body and psychic impulses born of sex equipment and sex desire that operate upon the emotions and influence the behavior. There is no need of a Freud to demonstrate that personality is saturated with sex from the early days of childhood to the very end of life. Its expression is inevitable but cumulative. After the individual has crossed into puberty no life-program, no conspiracy of silence, can shut it out, although it is not difficult for the young man or woman to refuse to admit its presence or to deal with it openly.

No small part of the stress that the unmarried experience on account of the surging of sex impulse is due to the general unwillingness of the social code to recognize this premarriage significance of sex desire, at least so far as the woman is concerned. As we shall see, changes are taking place, but the pervading and controlling notion still carries the suggestion that sex before marriage is a faulty breaking out of impulses that should be so tamed, that is, so suppressed, as not to constitute any serious problem in the well-adjusted.

Because this attitude adds to the difficulties of American youth, it must not be inferred that those who, through exceptionally early training or from adolescent sophistication, are thoroughly acquainted with the strength and normality of their sex impulses are entirely free from any tension. It proves an advantage for sex to be out in the open, but there still remains the task of adjusting either to the orthodox social code or to a self-made, consistent program of conduct. The frequency and the tenseness of this type of conflict must not betray us into thinking that all adolescent struggle takes this form or is of sex origin. The career of adolescence, through the interaction of the individual and the group, provides many occasions for tension, and sometimes even those brought about by social circumstances find a sex expression.

It might seem that no American young person, when sex flares forth from every direction, could possibly escape coming to know the personal impulses that thrust themselves into consciousness as a result of the outer social, or the inner body sex-stimulations, or both working together. It is indeed strange that anyone can avoid the environmental awakening of consciousness of sex when the physical and psychic preparedness for this experience is so thoroughly established. Yet this happens. The observing person does not need to go far afield to find evidence of such extraordinary blindness to the forces operating. The mind has been made so resistant through early teaching that, although the barrier against the penetration of sex is thinner than paper and of no protection, there is complete anesthesia so far as the significance of sex awakening is concerned, an utter absence of frank attention to what is taking place.

This obtuseness to a very significant, and possibly

the most compelling part of the individual's life, uncovers the length to which conditioning of sex may go and the sensitiveness sex normally has in childhood to adult pressure. Through such extreme illustrations we come to see that society is chiefly responsible for the premarriage sex tension of youth. This realization of the origin of the strain does not solve the problems of life for either the child, the unmarried adolescent, the unmarried adult, or those in process of domestic adjustment. Since much of this coercion of early sex that causes conflict is inherent in civilization itself, it cannot be erased unless man is stripped of much of his cultural possessions. This fact does not forbid a more rational program, but only the unthinking optimist supposes that the wisest, most scientific of sex education connotes the entire elimination of the stress which those who pass through puberty encounter in one form or another.

The humanizing process which has taken man so far away from his animal origin has extended and refined the sex impulse which originally was so closely tied to reproduction and so thoroughly subservient to it. This spread has increased the opportunities of sex stimulation. Meanwhile, there has been an exploiting of the opportunity that this provides for entrance into the inner life of individuals through suggestions that in subtle or crude form are essentially sexual in character. These suggestions as they are used in modern life to motivate action are often so diluted as not to seem related to sex until they are given a thoroughgoing analysis. As modern men and women have grown more open to sex stimulation there has been corresponding development in the skillful use of this appeal through such popular mediums as, for example, illustrated advertising and the movies. It is because of this that civilization in these days seems so highly sexed.

The transference of physical sex energy to psychic expression so often takes place and is so readily accomplished that it seems to be a symptomatic feature of modern life. It is least apparent in the peasant Negroes of the South, who, by their lack of inhibition of physical sex, are little troubled by tension. They obtain their escape at the cost of arresting their sex life on the plane of meager content.

The ease with which stimulations on the physical level come out in psychic derivatives hides the extent of the sex life of the unmarried. The unexpected recoil of some men or women from a fellowship which has been accepted as an erotic substitute for body impulses, when this intimacy has led to the stimulating of physical desire, reveals that emotions may move in either direction. The transference from friendship to passion is made so rapidly and so completely that many a young man or young woman is forced without warning to a disturbing self-discovery and for the first time comes to feel the strength of a sex drive that is both physical and psychic.

There is no standard sex career before marriage and no safe generalization which assumes a norm in either the strength or the spread of sex impulse. We find variation both among the married and the unmarried. People range from an apparent frigidity to a sex dominance that strangles every other impulse. These two radical variations may be regarded as abnormal. Between them there appears a distribution of conscious sex drive from almost utter absence to intense vigor. It must be remembered that this curve represents the suppression or the awareness of sex rather than its absence or presence. Sex may meet with such strength of resistance, established and developed from childhood, that it remains hidden not only from others but from the individual himself. It is so thoroughly buried that it seems to have disappeared. It flows, however, underneath, much as does water beneath the earth's surface. Those individuals who seem to be devoid of the sex urge are usually less free and consistent than appears to the observer. Rarely are they without their problems; they merely have transferred sex from its legitimate field of expression to some psychic trait where it remains unrecognized. We may discover flaws in a personality, but because they have no apparent connection with sex we may not realize their origin but assume instead that the sex impulse has failed to develop or that during the child's early impressionable period it was strangled.

In addition to the personal differences which are as great as in any feature common to humanity, we need also to keep in mind the effect of age, which also has its personal curve of distribution. At the onset of puberty, for example, in the boy and the girl we detect evidences of the new physiological awakening and disturbance of the body, and, accompanying this under normal circumstances, the beginning of heterosexual attraction. The content of sex experience, in spite of rapid change in the body and the new tension, is meager. It accumulates meaning as maturity proceeds. Here we encounter the dilemma that seems likely always to challenge youth. If no barriers to public impulses are erected and sex turns entirely into physical channels, its development ceases and the erotic life in the large sense is retarded, if not arrested. This explains the limited domestic achievements of those who, like some of the Negroes of the rural South or peasants of Europe, make courtship also an experimental mating. On the other hand, the program that permits the spreading and the deepening of the erotic craving cannot help bringing forth tension and may, because adults lack sympathy and insight, turn sex impulse toward some morbid trend. Other groups in their effort to escape tension may flee from the conflict-making dilemma of unsatisfied impulse on the one hand and conventions on the other and may turn to some substitution for their erotic craving, often work or ambition, only to find periodically that sex or love impulses break into their security and force the recognition of inner stress. This invasion, by often becoming the cause of anxiety, shame or guilt feeling, not only warps sex development but wars against the integrity of the individual.

There is also another complication which may be described best as periodicity. Certainly after puberty, more apparently in the woman than in the man, there are changes that conform to a cycle which is thoroughly individual. Sex may show great vigor as an impulse and after a few days pass to an apparent oblivion. This happens even though the changes do not take an overt sexual form. There are differences in personal emotion, differences in the individual's efficiency, differences in the pleasure-tone of the personality, even though their connection with the sex rhythm may not be recognized by the individual or by those about him.

There are two sides to sex tension, and there is need of understanding the social pressure as well as the physiological urge. It is a most fortunate child who passes safely through his contacts with adults in his early years without having shame or some degree of guilt-feeling incorporated into his sex development. It is as if sex, having proved too much for adults, brings forth an uncontrollable anxiety when they first discover its appearance in their child. The reception that is accorded the faintest curiosity of the child at the moment when he distinguishes the sex equipment either of himself or of some other shows how intense and how irrational is the reaction of the average parent who is conscious of his responsibility for the sex guidance of his children. Both religious and ethical leaders are open to the same temptation and may react with such emotion or exaggeration to any expression of interest by the child as to encourage in the growing personality a morbid undercurrent regarding sex. This danger of socially perverting the normal sex impulses has grown less in recent years as parents have become better informed and more understanding. On the other hand, there have been added difficulties due to the special circumstances that beset modern parents.

We live in a time when the tempo of existence has in itself become a problem, not because it is inherently troublesome but on account of our lack of seasoning. The onrush of the modern way of living has been so sudden that we are open to its dangers, having had no time to build an immunity through contact. Every feature of our civilization reveals this. It is not, therefore, to be expected that the sex life should escape, and clearly it has not. One of the consequences is the rapid sophistication of the average boy and girl and the thrusting upon them of more mature sex knowledge and stimulation than they would have encountered at such an age in former times. We are apt to forget how rapidly we expect our young people to pass from the attitudes characteristic of the child to the social responsibilities of an adult living on the complex level of modern life. It is not strange that the more primitive impulses balk at this refinement, that there is frequently a turning back to fantasy and to standards of behavior that reveal an unsatisfied curiosity and an eager effort to understand sex.

The rapid flow of social change has swept away traditions that formerly regulated and established standards for the sex career of the unmarried. It is much like the river in the spring flood that has so changed its banks that the most experienced pilot finds none of the landmarks by which he has been in the habit of tracing his course. Sex no more than other expressions of the modern man's and woman's life escapes the difficulties of this rapid change, but what happens in this field of human experience is perhaps socially most disturbing. Sex has always been rigorously guarded by social tradition. It has been group coercion rather than individual self-discipline that has chiefly controlled sex conduct in the past, with the result that always, in a period of transition, sexual unrest, experimentation and confusion have been greatest. A considerable part of the psychic conflict of the individual reflects our social situation in this period of transition. The fact that the mores themselves are in confusion adds to the difficulties of those, who, sensitive to the social traditions and group coercions, are seeking to establish personal harmony. The task of establishing inner concord, as the primitive impulses seem to press one way and social demands the other—always difficult—is made all the greater by the prevailing social unrest and cultural disturbances of this time of rapid change.

In spite of the breaking of taboo, enough shy evasion has persisted to hamper the frank preparatory discussion of sex that young people have greatly needed in order to pass most easily through their ordeal. Feeling often only that they are out of all accord with their parents' attitudes, young men and women, meeting the full blast of machine culture, have seldom received the sympathy and understanding that they have needed to give them confidence in handling the personal problems of sex that have been forced upon them. They have been thrown into a loneliness that is unparalleled in human evolution.

In spite of this handicap, a multitude of young women and a sizable group of men, conscious of sex, have deliberately worked out a program which in most cases they have tested, often abandoned quickly, and in other cases incorporated in their later and more mature philosophy of life. Some, unwilling to reduce sex to mere physical passion, have frankly faced their body drive and, while waiting for marriage, sublimated it; others have accomplished the same task but without realizing what they were doing. In both cases the process has been essentially that of the projection of sex into other realms of conduct and interest. Sex energy is put to other uses. It acts like water turned away from the river channel and directed by the canal to the mill wheel. Sex pulsation is made a source of power to carry on lines of activity that are not at all related to the force from which they draw part of their motive and their strength.

This projection has proceeded along two different lines. One has been through the attempt to forget the turmoil of the self and to drown out the demands of sex by transference. The other projection has been through the substitution of an available relationship for that not possible, and has taken the form of fixation. The first program is commonly interpreted as a sublimation of sex. It has attracted both the man and the woman, but more often the latter. Although it takes myriad expressions, they all may be roughly classified as work, sport, or artistic creation. Many a business woman is earning more than self-support through her concentration on her daily vocation. She is also driving sex out of consciousness either fully or in part by her work. Philanthropy, science, and religion are all utilized for the same purpose and provide psychic relief in the same way. The arts provide another favored means of lessening tension. It may be either the attempt to produce for oneself in music, in painting or in literature, or it may take the less ambitious form of appreciation of the work of others. The dance also serves the same useful purpose.

Sex is also externalized and suppressed by substituting a relationship which at least has a semblance of erotic fellowship. This is the higher, the more difficult, and the more successful of the two programs. Friends, one or both parents, other people's children are the most common persons chosen for fellowship in this way of escaping strain of sex origin. If the former method carries the risk of being swept aside at any moment when sex is thoroughly aroused, this projection upon persons tends toward the danger of becoming essentially itself a sexual relation, although not admitted to be such. The fact that it is an intimate exclusive relationship permits the erotic love cravings to flow freely in a disguised form. Physiological sex is pushed into the background but psychological sex may become the very essence of the fixation. From this come tragedies. If tension is escaped for a time, it may surge again with even greater strength and with no apparent way of escape.

Throughout the sex career of the unmarried, in a great majority of cases, marriage is the goal toward which the heart is set, even when it seems far away and perhaps beyond attainment. Matrimony is nearly always the one thing most desired, at least as the finale of the first chapter of life. This thought of the ideal ultimate fulfillment has all the force of eager anticipation. By most men it is looked forward to as a certainty. In the hope of the average woman, on the contrary, there is nearly always a mixture of doubt, a recognition of the possibility of being turned aside and forced to a continuous program of sublimation. Fortunately, there is evidence of a growing freedom which permits women to express more frankly and more directly, after the manner of men, their interest in the finding and the winning of their mate. This lessens their feeling of uncertainty by offering opportunity for aggressive initiative without the necessity of putting on the former mask of subtlety.

Although no period of life is more positive and more demanding than that stretching from early puberty to marriage, it is nearly always felt to be transitory, a prelude, negative in character as compared with the experiences of marriage. Matrimony is thought of as the socially fulfilling experience. Sex would not be nearly so great a problem during the premarriage years if youth could take that period seriously as a preparatory stage, providing opportunity for the gaining of self knowledge and an understanding of the other sex in readiness for marriage. The tension drives imagination, and thought becomes occupied with the idea of the ultimate outcome, marriage, with the result that the value of the period as a preparation is at least lessened when it is not largely lost. Failure to gain the insight required for marriage, inability to discipline and mature sex and to establish standards, or a precocious commitment to sex experience that does not travel beyond its physiological origin, often brings the man or woman to the testing of marriage thoroughly unprepared to meet the new responsibility and to accomplish the adjustment that successful marriage requires.

The failure to achieve a love attachment, or the necessity of a continuous postponement of marriage after one has fallen in love, easily leads to a feeling of inferiority that reveals itself in social attitudes entirely detached from any apparent sex connection. The first of these has been a problem for many young women throughout the history of American society. The second more often disturbs the young man now than was formerly the case. The closing of the frontier, the more rigid and more competitive organization of industry, the longer period required for preparation for the professions and the lifting of the general standard of life, forces many men to delay marrying, especially in the cities and in the middle class. This inability, for economic reasons, to start marriage affects both the young man and woman, but since ordinarily the first is expected to supply the necessary income, his failure to attain the position where he can do this reacts more upon him than upon the woman. One of the happy trends at present appears in the increasing willingness of young people to meet this problem by establishing an economic partnership which enables them to marry on a united income made possible by the continuance of both in gainful employment. It may be only a temporary compromise between a limited family life and none at all, but it prevents the many dangers and much of the tension of a postponed wedding.

The delay of marriage because of economic insecurity is leading to experimentation in sex relations and an attempt at a substitute for marriage. These sociological consequences of the inability to marry on account of insufficient income also have psychological meaning. There are reactions in the feeling that one is drifting away from marriage, or cannot hope to marry until many years have passed, found chiefly in the middle class among the young men and women of business or professional training. Not infrequently the attempted solution of a substitute for marriage leads all the more to the building of a chronic feeling of inferiority. The woman may come to see or to think that she is attractive only on a physical basis and that she is more removed than ever from mating on account of having accepted a liberal code of conduct. One gets the impression that the man is more likely to feel the ethical or psychic strain of behavior which collides with orthodox practices, and if he is less liable to a feeling of inferiority in comparison with the woman, he is the more open to emotional conflict, especially when he discovers that the relations he intended to keep on the level of physical comradeship have been regarded by the woman as assurance or at least as a basis for hopes of the development of an erotic fellowship that includes their marrying eventually.

The consequences of the depression have added to the burden that the present transitional state of American culture puts upon many of our young people. The psychic aspects of sex among the unmarried are such as always to invite situations that lead to the building of feelings of inferiority and to the coming of emotional conflicts. There is still little realization in our social thinking of the effect of adding to this disturbance that comes from the unparalleled onsweep of cultural changes, the denial of marriage, or its repeated postponements for financial reasons. Unless there is soon a lessening of this economic veto of the hope of marrying, the seriousness of the present situation will be increasingly laid bare. If monogamic standards are to be maintained, without any considerable competition from temporary forms of sex alliance, a more constructive social program must be established, making it easier for young people to marry than is the present vogue.

# SOCIOLOGY

But, as in the long run the prosperity of any social group will depend upon the individual acts of each of its members, this or that code of manners will at last be the means of bringing about the extinction or the survival of a tribe, struggling for existence against its rivals. . . . Promiscuity, polygamy, polyandry, partial marriages—obliging those joined together for a portion only of the week or of the month, and permitting simultaneously a dozen or twenty unions—monogamy, exogamic marriage, and endogamic marriage, all these will be found to exist capriciously in the different human societies. . . . The noblest forms of connubial life are not, in our opinion, always the sign of a high intellectual development.—CHARLES LETOURNEAU.

## SOCIOLOGICAL ASPECTS OF THE SEX LIFE OF THE UNMARRIED ADULT

*Ernest W. Burgess*

PROFESSOR OF SOCIOLOGY,

UNIVERSITY OF CHICAGO

THE SEX life of the unmarried adult is studied by the sociologist in its social rather than in its biological aspects. This general point of view with reference to sex is clearly set forth by William Graham Sumner.

He points out that the sex relation among all peoples has always been subject to definition and redefinition by the *mores*.

The sex passion has two opposite extremes,—renunciation and license. In neither one of these can peace and satisfaction be found, or escape from the irritation of antagonistic impulses.

The sex relation has been a great arena for the use and perfection of the mores, since personal experience and reflection never ceased, and a great school for the education of the race in the use of intelligence, the development of sympathetic sentiments, and in a sense of the utility of ethical regulations. The sex taboo is the set of inhibitions which control and restrain the intercourse of the sexes with each other in ordinary life. At the present time, in civilized countries, that intercourse is limited by taboo, not by law. The nature and degree of the taboo are in the mores. Spanish, French, English, and American women, in the order named, are under less and less strict limitations in regard to ordinary social intercourse with men. The sex taboo could, therefore, be easily pursued and described through the whole history of civilization and amongst all nations. It seems to be arbitrary, although no doubt it has always been due, in its origin, to correct or incorrect judgments of conditions and interests. It is always conventional. That it has been and is recognized is the sum of its justification.

Accordingly, the following sort of questions intrigues the sociologist:

In the culture of any given people what are the sanctioned and the taboo forms of sex behavior?

What social rôle is assigned to the adult unmarried person?

How great is the social pressure upon the individual to conform to group expectations of his conduct?

Within a given culture, what variations in sex behavior occur in different social groups?

To what extent are the so-called problems or pathology of the sex life of adult unmarried persons the result of cultural conditioning rather than of biological tendencies or psychological impulsion?

In raising these and other questions it is fully conceded that the sociological point of view is only a partial one and that a complete explanation of the sex life of the unmarried requires a synthesis with all the other approaches: biological, psychological, economic, anthropological.

History has witnessed great changes in the rôle in society of the unmarried adult. Only in recent years and in modern societies has the so-called "single" person achieved a recognized independent social status.

Typically, at least among historical peoples, the single state was but a temporary transition into marriage. It was assumed that youth normally would marry and that the few unmarried persons, old maids and bachelors, would live in a dependent status within some family circle.

The single person, then, with an independent status in society is peculiarly a phenomenon of modern times. Bachelor apartments and clubs with comfortable rooming quarters were at first provided only for men, and not until recently for women. There has been a great increase in apartment and residential hotels catering not only to married couples but to unmarried men or women who perforce, or by preference, no longer live under the parental roof.

Where marriages are arranged by the parents, as in the Orient, the unmarried adult is conspicuous by his absence. In European medieval society the institutionalized form of unmarried life with its vow of celibacy was found in the priesthood and in the monastery and the convent.

In American society the young people early took the control of courtship and marriage into their own hands. The institution of courtship had two outstanding effects upon the social life of unmarried adults.

In the first place, it greatly encouraged social contacts of the sexes before marriage. This inevitably led to certain changes in sexual attitudes and behavior that will be discussed later.

In the second place, the introduction of choice of partners by young people rather than by parents naturally increased the difficulty of concluding engagements and marriages. Two groups of single persons created by this factor are to be distinguished: (a) the single by preference, and (b) the single by failure in the competition for marriage. This might lead us to expect that the number of unmarried in the marriageable population would increase. On the contrary, however, there has been a decline in the proportion of bachelor men and women in each decade, and almost without exception in each age group, from 1890 to 1930. Today in the age group from forty-five to sixty-four, only eleven per cent are unmarried.

The sex life of the unmarried adult may be treated under four major divisions:

1. The evolution of the American attitude toward sex and romance.

2. Studies of the sex life of youth before marriage.

3. Inquiries into the sex life of older unmarried adults.

4. Research in the sex life of special groups of unmarried adults.

## 1. EVOLUTION OF THE AMERICAN ATTITUDE TOWARD SEX AND ROMANCE

Changes in attitude toward sex and romance in this country should be studied with an understanding of the social definitions of sex and sexual behavior in a given culture. W. I. Thomas and Florian Znaniecki depict the cultural conditioning of the premarital sex behavior of the Polish peasant, which differs widely from American norms. The Puritan tradition enforced a taboo upon sex discussion and instruction, emphasized the supreme value of chastity before marriage, particularly for women, and refused to recognize the resulting problems in the sex life of the married and the unmarried.

Historically, the evolution of the American attitude toward sex and romance may be traced through three periods which may perhaps be schematically identified by the social situations of the rural neighborhood, the town and the city.

(a) *Courtship in the rural neighborhood.* The transition from marriages dictated by parents to marriages arranged by young people at first represented little personal freedom of choice. The group code governing courtship was almost as rigid as parental pressure. "Keeping company" or "going together steady" resulted from slight indications of preference and led almost inevitably to engagement and engagement led to marriage. "Falling in love" was the *sine qua non* for marriage as defined by the mores. In general, although by no means universally, but at least in theory, the physical aspects of sex were minimized before marriage. The common term in use for the technique of courtship was "sparking," which carries its own implications. The popular novels of the Reverend E. P. Roe, of the seventies and eighties, conveys a sense of the approved patterns of relationships among young people.

The Reverend Roe was a valiant champion of the rural virtues and an unsparing critic of the vices of the city which were causing widespread alarm in outraged Puritan circles. Rural readers were doubtless also thrilled by their vicarious experience of the romantic perils of the city portrayed by him. He was much more interested in the moral lesson to be derived from his popular books (the previously unheard-of number of 1,400,000 were sold before his death) than in their literary style. The standards of conduct upheld in his works and the moral and religious spirit in which they were written is thus expressed in his own words in the preface to one of his novels, *What Can She Do?*

If I in my little sphere can by this book lead one father to train his children to be more strong and self-reliant, one mother to teach her daughters a purer, more patient, more heroic womanhood—if I have placed one more barrier in the tempter's way, and inspired one more wholesome fear and principle in the heart of the tempted—if, by lifting the dark curtain a moment, I can reveal enough to keep one country girl from leaving her safe native village for unprotected life in some great city—if I can add one iota toward a public opinion that will honor useful labor, however humble, and condemn and render disgraceful idleness and helplessness, however gilded—if, chief of all, I lead one heavy-laden heart to the only source of rest, I shall be well rewarded, whatever is said of this volume.

He was against women's attempt to enter the industrial and political arena because "in the sphere of quiet homes—not elsewhere—I believe that women can best rule and save the world."

Romance in the rural neighborhood was but a brief prelude to matter-of-fact marriage, with all the prosaic routine of farm life. The long hours of rural labor left little time during courtship and less in marriage for social relations. Marriage itself was an economic necessity and partnership; children were necessary as "hands" in the operation of the farm.

(b) *Courtship in the town.* In the towns and cities marriage tended to be delayed and the period of courtship and engagement to be extended. With the growing economic independence of youth, their social life became an end in itself.

Sex became somewhat more a self-conscious interest, with some freedom of experimentation, conventionally restricted to engaged couples. Coquetry, flirting, and playing at love entered into the social interaction of young people. The term "spooning" was current during this period and described the permissible and expected, if not altogether approved, behavior during courtship and engagement.

The popular novels, influencing and expressing the attitudes and behavior of youth in this period, are those, among others, of Harold Bell Wright, Gene Stratton Porter, and Robert W. Chambers. In the novels of Mr. Wright and Mrs. Porter, the strong, virile, simple traits of manhood of the heroes and the sweet, tender, virtuous and true qualities of womanhood of the heroines inspired and uplifted millions of persons young and old, although they nauseated the intellectual minority who inveighed against the bad literary taste and moral sentimentality of the great American middle class. *The Winning of Barbara Worth,* by Wright, and *Freckles, The Girl of the Limberlost, The Harvester,* and *Laddie,* by Porter sold in the unprecedented numbers of a million and a half to two million copies each.

For the more sophisticated of the middle class, especially in the cities, Robert W. Chambers, according to H. L. Mencken, "with his 'society' romances for shop-girls," popularized through the medium of serials in *The Saturday Evening Post* and other magazines, vividly delineated the newer, and at that time, quite daring, techniques in the art of love.

(c) *Courtship in the city.* Urbanization in the United States has proceeded apace in the past forty years. New instruments of transportation and communication have revolutionalized social life, particularly for youth.

The automobile has broken down the rigid control of personal gossip. It has widened the area of social contacts from a radius of five to one hundred miles. In large cities the neighborhood dance hall has swiftly declined, as palaces of the Terpsichorean art are thronged with a city-wide attendance. Through the radio the wider outside world has invaded even the sacred precincts of the home, undermining familial control and traditional standards.

The great increase since the war in the number of multi-family dwellings has made more acute the problem of privacy. Data also indicate that the number of rooms per apartment is decreasing. Courting can no longer be carried on, as under rural and town conditions, at home in the "front parlor," but takes place in public parks, in parked automobiles, in public dance halls, in motion picture theatres, in cabarets, in night clubs and in road houses.

Recent research by Blumer, as reported in *Movies and Conduct,* most tellingly demonstrates the influence of the motion picture upon the sex attitudes and behavior of young people. The art of love as depicted by screen stars becomes the accepted pattern for emulation. Moreover, sexual impulses, freed from conventional inhibitions, find unrestrained expression in phantasy, and so tend to more and more individualized expression.

The effect of the automobile, the radio and the cinema are only the most evident expression of fundamental changes affecting all American life.

The change in the status of women to approximate equality with men, the economic and social emancipation of youth, the lifting of the taboo upon sex discussion are all part of a frame of reference necessary for a sociological inquiry into the love and sex life of the unmarried adult.

The outstanding attitude of modern youth emerging from his reaction to the forces impinging upon him is one of self-consciousness and sophistication about sex. Youth in this day and generation are rated in terms of sex appeal. The technique of "vamping" is freely discussed as well as means of protection against it. Beauty parlors have witnessed a tremendous growth. Charm classes are popular and are sponsored even by the Young Women's Christian Association. National advertising utilizes sex as perhaps its most enticing lure in baiting the attention of the buying public to its wares.

Instruction in sex, advocated as a solution of the

problems created by ignorance, has created others attendant upon both little and unlimited knowledge. Sexual expression and experimentation in varying degrees and in manifold forms, both subtle and overt, have greatly increased. The churches have removed the Puritan ban from social dancing. The Federal Council of Churches has given a guarded but unequivocal endorsement of the dissemination of birth-control information, although the American Medical Association remains silent upon this burning issue. "Petting" and "necking" are popular terms for a degree of physical intimacy between casual acquaintances that was not permitted engaged couples of earlier generations.

The Young Men's Christian Association appointed a Commission on Relations between College Men and Women which worked a year in preparation of a pamphlet entitled *The Sex Life of Youth.* "The question for all thoughtful youth," says the report, "is: what type and degree of physical-emotional intimacy, if any, is advisable before the more definite mutual commitment of one man and one woman to each other in engagement? What types of relations minister to increased understanding, self-command, and enrichment, and what types lead to confusion and emotional difficulties?"

This pamphlet was flippantly referred to in *The Nation* as "A Manual for Petters."

These three periods of courtship in the rural neighborhood, in the town and in the city denote stages in the evolution of American attitudes toward sex and romance. Conditions at present in the open country and in the town have been as profoundly affected by the automobile, the motion picture and the radio as those in our urban centers.

All evidence seems to point to a greater or less decline in the emphasis upon chastity before marriage. Undoubtedly, at present, this is more marked in attitude than in behavior, and varies widely from group to group.

There is no question, however, that the range of social contacts and the sexual knowledge and experience of youth before marriage is greater than in any previous generation.

## 2. STUDIES OF THE SEX LIFE OF YOUTH BEFORE MARRIAGE

Advocates of sexual instruction of children and youth argued that sex enlightenment would solve the problems of ignorance. They did not anticipate the problems that would arise from knowledge. In fact, they could hardly have foreseen the variety and range of sexual manifestations which have followed the raising of the sex taboo: proposals for trial marriage, sexual experimentation of youth, the increasing number of salacious books and magazines, the cult of nudism, the vogue of fan dancers, and so forth.

Sex, indeed, had come into its own. On the principle of ambivalence, over-repression was naturally followed by over-expression. It is, perhaps, easy to overemphasize this upward surge of sex without noting the quieter flow of more basic currents, more truly indicative of future trends. Indeed, there is evidence that even in the "whoopee" period of the prohibition era sex education in many middle-class homes was producing wholesome effects. This is apparent in the Report of the

White House Conference on Child Health and Protection.

Over 400 personal documents written anonymously by college men and women give an intimate account of parental education. An analysis of these documents revealed the marked gratitude of children to parents who imparted sex information to them and, correspondingly, resentment expressed in greater or less degree to parents who had withheld this knowledge.

It is difficult, if not impossible, to present any adequate picture of the trends during the past few decades in sex attitudes and behavior of adolescents and youth before marriage. This much is certain, that a complete picture involves the double analysis, (1) of certain major trends in American society as a whole, and (2) a minute inquiry into the various patterns of sexual ideals and standards of many divergent social groups of young people.

For the purposes of the present article, we may assume as motivating factors of change the following trends:

1. Lifting of the taboo upon sex discussion and the accompanying tendency to dissociate the satisfactions of sex from the expression of the other elements of the personality, frequently even from the affectional elements.

2. The increasing freedom of women, with the demand for moral and sexual, as well as economic and social emancipation.

3. The so-called revolt of youth as manifested in their demand to be considered as adults and the setting up of a social world of adolescents with its own peculiar characteristics, conceptions of life and standards of behavior.

Within the general frame of reference of changes in

the mores of social movements in American society, each homogeneous social group exerts its own determining impress upon the conduct of its members. The influence of the family, while it varies greatly from section to section, from city to country, from household to household within the same community, is relatively constant and consistent in the inculcation of the traditional ideals of family life. It is outside of the family that social groups show the greatest complexities and variations. For that reason, it may be expedient in attempting any summary comparison of sex attitudes and behavior before and after the World War, to focus attention upon the more apparent phases of the sex life of students in college and university communities.

An observer has written the following statement of the social life of young people in a college community of twenty-five years ago:

> This mid-western University is located in a state with a Puritan impress which was still quite marked in the years preceding the World War. Students thronged the local churches for Sunday School, morning and evening service. The different religious denominations maintained flourishing religious and recreational centers upon the campus itself.
>
> In contrast with this undoubtedly healthy religious and moral tone of the student body certain incidents during one year in which notes were kept are indicative of trends in sexual behavior and attitude. A young woman is shocked to find that in her sorority of thirty members she is the only one who would refuse to marry a suitor who had deviated from the single standard of morality. In a leading fraternity a truth session brought out admissions of sexual experiences from all but three of its twenty-five members.

In spite of active efforts at suppression on the part of the University administration a scandal sheet made its sensational appearance two or three times during the school year. Its contents were a curious combination of rebellion against the sexual taboo and of the reformist spirit of youth; subtle and not so subtle risqué jokes and epigrams, stories of double meaning, and most prominently featured, an exposé of the double life of campus "celebrities," men who were keeping company, at the same time, with respectable girls from the campus circle and town girls of doubtful reputation.

During the year there occurred certain incidents of greater or less notoriety. The local daily paper played up on its front page the details of the arrest of a prominent student who was a regular attendant at church. The news story gave the details of his arrest by the police in the act with a town girl in a local park. A landlady protested to the University authorities about the behavior of a student roomer who, without her knowledge, had inveigled a young working woman to his room for the night. Two freshman girls who had just failed of acceptance by a sorority were reported by those "in the know" as paying the price required for association with two of the big fraternity men of the campus.

The whole picture, to be true, is one of the relative wholesomeness of the social life of college young people with only occasional moral derelictions still held in rather tightly by prevailing Puritan sanctions.

This description, while fragmentary and incomplete, may serve to illustrate certain of the chief points in the social relation of the sexes in campus life before the World War:

1. The general wholesome state of social relationships

of a student body which is relatively homogeneous because of the common Puritan culture maintained by the home, the church and the school.

2. The demand for some freedom of sexual experimentation on the part of a certain proportion of college men and the expectation of virtuous behavior on the part of the co-ed.

3. The general student disapproval, coupled with some admiration, of the double life of those campus men who "kept company" with a college girl and had affairs at the same time with town girls.

4. Only sporadic instances are indicative of a revolt of the more daring against the accepted sex norms of the community.

The changes occurring in the post-war situation may perhaps be most strikingly observed in the sophistication and extremes of behavior among certain groups of high-school students. The following four cases of high-school situations show group patterns as well as marked individual differences in behavior. The first was written by a high-school girl, fifteen years of age.

When I became a freshman in high school I met a boy named Tom who was very nice to me. We used to study together and have very good times. I liked him very much and he liked me.

We got along finely until he began to go with a crowd that I couldn't stand. They used to think nothing but "dirt." The stories and language they used were really vile. They even used to kid us girls about our monthly sicknesses and make suggestive remarks.

The boys used to try to take the girls' skirts off whenever they would get a chance and they would laugh at us when we objected. Even the girls I knew got dirty-minded by association with these boys and used to tell stories that were quite smutty. I can appreciate a good dirty joke as well as anyone and can be a good sport but these jokes weren't even funny. I couldn't talk like that even though I did not want to be considered prudish. They just went too far.

One day all of this bunch went out in the park and they asked me to go along. Tom wasn't able to go but I went just the same. Everything was all right until it got dark. Then some of the boys got fresh with the girls and the one that was with me became too free with his hands. I could stand some of that from Tom but I didn't like this boy. Finally I got so disgusted that I asked him to take me home. He refused to do it, so I went home alone.

Since that time I haven't had anything to do with these kids or with Tom. I would have gone with Tom but he wouldn't give up going with that gang and besides he got too much like them to suit me.

To play the "clock game" everyone obtained a card on which was inscribed a circle to represent the dial of a clock and the twelve numbers which represent hours. High school boys would make "dates" with the girls for each of these "hours" and meet the girls when the right time was called. The time presumably was spent in conversing. With the more proper of the girls we stayed in the gymnasium or in the assembly hall, with the others we sought hallways, cloakrooms, forgotten corners and the like. At one of these "hours" I obtained my first kiss—and my fifth or eighth as well. When we became wiser we would arrange with suitable girls for several consecutive hours. At another time, three couples, all of us "steadies," arranged our entire program among ourselves, got a classroom and locked the door behind us to insure privacy. This gave us an excellent op portunity to pet, which we did, curiously enough, by changing off among ourselves. This incident, I may add, occurred while I was a sophisticated senior in high school. *(Written while a college student.)*

One of the prettiest girls in school had persuaded a friend to bring me, a newcomer, to the party. Afterward, the four of us drove to a lonely spot and parked. My girl and I necked mildly for an hour or two and then they drove me home. I was elated and extremely pleased by the experience. The next day a mutual acquaintance told me that his girl had said, "He (myself) is terrible. He doesn't even know how to work a girl up." A few other boys who were present laughed heartily. I was mortified and chagrined and said, "Work her up? I didn't try to work her up. I thought she was a decent girl." *(Written by a high-school graduate.)*

In a western city it is now traditional for high-school boys to patronize houses of prostitution. By graduation the large majority not only have received their sexual initiation in this way but many have already become regular patrons. *(A report on prostitution.)*

These four cases are only samples of a larger array which would indicate both the general increase in sexual sophistication of adolescents and marked differences by individuals, by social groups, by cities, and even by communities within cities. For example, the early initiation in sex via the house of prostitution as described above is not typical of high-school students in American cities in general.

While high-school experience gives the background for the college situation, a powerful factor of selection operates. The ninth grade exacts a high toll of failures which falls heaviest upon the fast crowd among the Freshmen. Consequently, only a fraction of those who enter high school graduate. Of those who graduate, only a fraction go on to college.

The number of students in our colleges and universities greatly increased after the War. For this and other reasons the college and university community is not the homogeneous closed-in society that it once was. So significant was the automobile as one of the factors destructive of the old-time solidarity of the college community and control of college discipline that several institutions of higher learning forbade students the use of cars.

Accordingly, it is much more difficult to present typical cases or to make generalizations now than for the period three decades ago. Sex is at present an open subject for discussion and reparteé among mixed groups, but each college group sets its own limits and these may be and are widely divergent. Exactly the same may be said for the social events of small, intimate groups which may vary from tame parties under church auspices through "petting" and "necking" parties to adventurous flings with gin and strip poker parties.

The following short summarized extracts from personal documents of college students therefore must be regarded as merely indicative of the sex life of college undergraduates.

The question of women continued to be purely a moral issue with me. My parents had clearly defined the relations between the sexes as being primarily on a spiritual level and incontinence before marriage as the paramount sin open to man. My father had called me aside once in my youth and explained to me the importance of coming to marriage with a pure body and a free conscience. My early high-school gang life brought certain lapses from the high ideal held up to me but I never lost the ideal. The fear of pregnancy or disease never worried me for my ideal stood between me and such possibilities. My fraternity brothers evidenced no inhibitions such as I had and they frequently indulged in questionable relations with girls about the college. I was horrified to find that one of the fellows who was engaged to a pretty girl on campus was having relations with other outside girls. How a fellow could love a girl and behave in this manner was beyond my comprehension.

It was only in my senior year at college that I found out about contraceptives. One Sunday evening a doctor came to the fraternity house, and let us ask him questions. We asked him questions for four hours, and then continued for three more after he had left. Then I found out for the first time that half the men living in the house had had sexual intercourse. Since that time my sex education has been rapid.

Having broken down the inhibition to talk about sex that night in the fraternity, and having been given enough data to be able to start a discussion at any time, and because I know so much about the subject, I can always assume the rôle of a person who has had much experience myself, and so men will talk frankly with me. Incidentally, I have read some Havelock Ellis since that time, some Marie Stopes, and one or two others. I still have the childhood inhibition about freedom in sex relationships, though, and have not yet broken them down.

My sex experience began during the summer after my freshman year in college. I was spending the summer at manual labor in the vicinity of the college town, and living in town. There were about a dozen students who remained in town for the summer. We lived in a close group. I was the only freshman in the group and was also several years younger than the group as a whole, and not socially mature enough to be really on their plane. I developed a considerable feeling of inferiority, although this was mostly subconscious, and this led to my desire to make myself more thoroughly grounded in affairs of life. . . . Also, I was very curious as to exactly what sexual intercourse was like. Therefore I proceeded to pick up one of the college widows and find out what life was about; having found out, I decided that it did not live up to the glowing specifications which I had heard about it, and proceeded to forget about it for almost a year, as far as any actual intercourse was concerned, although of course I pondered on it frequently.

The following summer I was employed in a hotel. By this time I was imbued with the biological outlook on life so prominent in the heroes and heroines of Scott Fitzgerald and Ernest Hemingway (although these characters never served as models to me—I arrived at this state independently) and I entered into the thrill of the chase with no moral scruples. By this time I had lost the idea of sex as something inherently bad; I must admit that I saw nothing constructive in it, either; my attitude was "some people call it love, but I call it a reflex."

Of the women whom I have known since then, the great majority have been lower in the social scale than myself but I have never been out with a prostitute. Of the ten women with whom I have had intercourse in the last four years, only three have had an education comparable to my own, and only two have meant very much to me. Although these affairs have been strictly matters of convenience, the response relationships have increased until I have succeeded in romanticizing all except two or three affairs whose crudeness repelled me.

I am unwilling to take the responsibilities of marriage; I am not in contact with a social group in which I could sublimate much of these desires, and as a result I have turned into the ways of comparative promiscuity, which is a rather unsatisfactory substitute.

The practice of "picking up women for purposes of sexual relations is widespread among college men. In many groups one who has had considerable sexual experience with women wears a pseudo-aura of prestige. The smutty story is as common on the campus as among the working classes. Sexual relations with a professional prostitute are frowned upon. The man is charged with being unable to win a woman. There is more talk of sex and fewer actual relations among campus men than among men of the same age in other classes of society.

College women in general do not engage in sexual relations. There are exceptions, however, in individuals and in groups. An extreme case is that of a precocious young girl of the intellectual type who in one year and two months has been mistress of nine men, five of whom had been virgins. Not infrequently, engaged couples drift into sexual relations which may or may not necessitate abortion. A few free-love groups, usually of the philosophical or adventurous type, are to be found in the student body. In these, virginity is ridiculed as a relic of a prudish age which is past. A girl who is promiscuous, however, as it becomes known, tends to lose caste in the group. A college woman who was a member of one of these rather loosely organized social groups summed up her philosophy as follows: "A woman has as much right to sexual freedom as a man. When two persons are congenial, and the understanding is clear, then there is little danger of mutual incrimination, unwarranted expectations, and emotional 'kick-back.'"

Ministers in the pulpit, priests at the altar, educators and lecturers on the platform, say it is easy to control yourself in a compromising situation: Be virile, yet be moral (which is a contradiction in terms). Either they never had temptation, or they are hypocrites or some few perhaps control themselves. When there are dim lights; voluptuous music of a jazz band; alcoholic stimulation; the pulsing contact with breasts; the thrill and magnetism of virile young bodies; the girl's warm, moist lips pressed against your own; the clinging pressure of the girl's slim legs and body; her enchanting odor; you are lashed to a frenzy of sex urge as though you had taken a powerful aphrodisiac from the insidious Orient. The path of resistance is hard; the path of pleasure is easy.

The changes in the sexual life of the student body, seen in the perspective of three decades, but reflect the trends operating in extra-mural society. Other movements have paralleled the great growth of popular interest in sex and sex education, in mental hygiene and in psychoanalysis, in child study and in training for parenthood. Paradoxically, the banning of the saloon brought about the "whoopee" period followed by repeal and the tavern. In *Vice in Chicago,* Walter C. Reckless describes the decline of brothel prostitution, but also the rise of the cabaret, the road-house, the night club and the increase in the "class of the independent, the emancipated, the clandestine prostitutes who want the life 'without its stigma and hardships.'"

It is in this setting of social change that the sex life of the unmarried adult is to be observed and studied.

With the passing of the frontier, spirited and adventurous youth was avid for thrilling and stimulating activities. For many adults as well as for adolescents, for experienced adventurers as well as amateurs, sex is the last *terra incognita,* full of the allurements and perils, surprises and disappointments, successes and tragedies of exploration. Yet in entering upon this adventure, the adolescent and the youth in general proceed not as individuals but as members of the group. In fact, the pattern of behavior, the code of conduct, the actual undertaking of the experience, appear often as phenomena of group determinism, showing, however, in many cases the influence of the family in conflict with that of the intimate social group.

Dolly June always caused a great deal of talk in the crowd. The other girls confined themselves to one crush at a time; not so Dolly June. She'd spoon through one dance with one boy and through the next with another; one boy would take her to a party and she'd jilt him for another on the way home. I ventured a remonstrance and her answer was, "They say no two boys kiss alike and I'm trying to find out if it is true. Besides it is lots of fun to let them think you are going to do a lot of things and then don't." In answer to my question, "Why do the boys let Dolly June treat them as she does?" one of the boys said, "Oh, that's just her line. She wants to neck all the time and no one fellow can stand it so we take turns."

After the last of the group had been out of high school about a year there seemed to be a change in the tone of the petting. The girls did not mention it so freely among themselves. The group began to pair off and both sexes showed embarrassment when accused of petting, even those who had petted openly a year or two before. The girls began to embroider guest towels and all sorts of things which they put in their "hope-chests." Dolly June was not paired with any of the boys in the crowd although there were one or two who seemed free. "Oh, Dolly June's all right," said the girls. "The boys like her, but she makes them tired." "Well, what's a fellow for unless to spend money and make the little creepies run up and down your back," was an expression heard so frequently from Dolly June that it was sometimes used instead of her name when she was referred to.

Because there was no boy in the village upon whom she could depend to take her to parties she began to stay in the city in the evening and go about with business acquaintances. After some months of this, she gave a party and introduced to the crowd a young man from the city. Before the evening was over, he was accepted as part of the crowd by the boys and the girls were full of curiosity. Some time later, after he had been out several times, one of the girls said, "I can't see how Dolly June attracted such a splendid fellow. He's fine—he has a good position, he can talk about all sorts of interesting things, different from our boys. I wonder if he really likes her. They're so different." *(Report of an observer.)*

This is a typical group situation. The lively girl with promiscuous tendencies is not sought in marriage in her intimate group but attracts an outsider who is not told of her reputation.

Several of the mates and engineers decided to go up to town for the evening and asked me to go along. I knew what was coming, for I knew their type. They landed in a cigar store which ostensibly was a soft drink and tobacco shop but which proved to be merely a blind for a house of prostitution. I had never joined in conversation about conquests of women or topics of sex experiences. So the fellows decided that they were going to make sure that they knew I was experienced to some extent. I dodged the question on the issue of money; but when the issue came again I pretended inebriation, for I actually had no desire for such experience. The last thing father had told me before I left home was: "If anyone tells you, son, that gonorrhea is no worse than a hard cold, you take the cold first." But it could not be avoided under the pressure exerted, and henceforth this particular group of fellows thought of me as one of them. *(Personal document.)*

I belonged to a gang of five fellows for two or three years from whom I learned many habits none too good for me and in whose company I had my first sex experiences with girls. The cultural conflict was strongest, I think, at this time between the ideals I had been taught and the ideals of our gang of which I was the recognized leader, but by no means the worst member. *(College student.)*

During my senior year at college I had become friendly with a fellow who had done a good deal of "bumming." His stories captured my imagination and I suggested that we 'hit the road' together immediately after convocation. Our first night away from home I had sexual intercourse for the first time in my life. In a little town, but a fast one, we met a gang of fellows who were impressed with what we were doing and entertained us royally. Part of the entertainment was a woman "who knew how to treat a fellow right." *(College student.)*

Of the hundred men in our company there were six without any bad habits, who did not smoke, drink, gamble, or go out with immoral women. There were, in addition, ten to fifteen who I know did not associate with women for the purpose of sexual intercourse. Loose women from all the small towns flocked into the camp cities. The behavior of the majority of the men was indifferent, depending on the men with whom they went out. About twenty-five of the men associated with Negro women. *(Ex-soldier, non-collegiate.)*

When a friend returned from the city he introduced our little group to a new type of literature—Rabelais, Gautier, James Branch Cabell. These men believed that love was something that could not, should not, be regulated by law. It was something beautiful beyond anything else, higher than anything else. When people loved they should give themselves to each other without regard for convention or marriage laws. Cabell thought that marriage inevitably killed true love, that no two people could endure the intimacy of married life and retain a pure love for each other. All this made a profound impression on me.

A few months afterward I was in love. By Christmas we had become very intimate and wanted each other desperately. I told the girl I could not marry for a long time, but that if we really loved each other I thought it would be all right if we had sexual relations. At first she refused, but when I told her that precautions could be taken to prevent anything happening, she agreed.

We have both been happier since but there have been disadvantages. We have to be very careful so no one will discover our relations, and then when we most want to be together I have to leave. As soon as I can afford it we will be married. I believe we shall be happy because we both realize the dangers of married life and will be prepared to meet them. (*Undergraduate student*)

### 3. SEX LIFE OF THE OLDER UNMARRIED ADULT

In the United States each succeeding age group shows a smaller proportion of unmarried males and females. In the later twenties and early thirties, the unmarried person may already have given up the expectation of marriage and have begun to conceive of himself in the rôle of the single man or woman.

Single men, as shown by statistics, are concentrated as farm hands in rural communities; as seasonal laborers, the so-called "hoboes" who hibernate in the cities in winter and are propelled out into the grain fields, railroad construction and lake transportation in the summer; and as residents of lodging houses and rooming houses in the cities.

Life histories of these single men show a wide range of sexual adjustment but with a distinct tendency to particularization in some form of sexual expression. This may vary from sublimation of sex or catharsis in some intense form of activity, economic, religious, humanitarian or radical; to autoerotic activity; to homosexual behavior of different types; to platonic friendships with women; to casual or regular affairs, permanent or promiscuous, with acquaintances and friends; adventures upon casual acquaintanceship with women seeking similar excitement and thrills; patronage of clandestine or of professional prostitutes. All these and other relationships are recognized social patterns of city life. Night clubs, taverns, beer flats, road houses, taxi dance halls, hotels and restaurants are institutions which frequently facilitate, and in turn profit from, illicit sexual adventure.

The emancipation of women brought with it the

opportunity for a career outside the family and the removal of much, if not all, of the invidious connotation of single existence. The term "bachelor woman" was substituted for "old maid."

The admission of women into the world of vocational activities seems at present to have resulted in occupational specialization by sex. Entire occupations like teaching, nursing, stenography, social work, have become almost entirely feminine in personnel, while the law, medicine and the ministry remain almost completely masculine.

Research into the sex life of the single woman is still in the pioneer stage. A study, *The Woman Who Waits,* by Frances Donovan, describes a situation where feminine charm, not infrequently an element in the remuneration of the waitress, gives ready possibilities, upon casual acquaintance, of invitation to thrilling and romantic, even if illicit, adventure. In the *Taxi Dance Hall,* Paul G. Cressey portrays a new occupation, the taxi dancer, in which feminine society is for sale at a dime a dance, for purchase by detached males, mostly unmarried, of the rooming-house areas of the large city. *The Saleslady,* also by Frances Donovan, presents a picture of an occupation, now well-organized, with a quite well-established separation between the business and the personal life of the saleswoman. The findings of this study indicate that saleswomen have now achieved a stable place in the business world, with the subordinating of their romantic impulses to the realities of economic life.

Life histories of women who voluntarily or involuntarily forego marriage for a vocational career frequently show dissatisfaction and restlessness in the field of response. Adjustments and maladjustments take varied form. More frequently, it seems, the conscious lack is more in the field of response, as, for example, expression of maternal love and care, than in direct sex expression itself.

Sublimation of sexual and maternal impulses may be observed in interest in nieces and nephews, in the adoption of children, in devotion to pets, in joint housekeeping with one or more other single women or in humanitarian and civic activities.

Friendships of the single woman with men are often of the platonic type, especially with those older or younger than herself. Unconventional relations have a large range of variation, including merely indiscreet or illicit, occasional or numerous, permanent or promiscuous affairs with close friends or casual acquaintances. In Bohemian groups and in rooming-house areas, in particular, more or less casual unions, of the philosophical free-love type, or more frequently of a practical economic sort, are not unusual. These variations depend mainly upon the standards of the group of which the woman is a member, but also seem to be partly determined by temperamental differences and personal individualization.

### 4. SEX LIFE OF SPECIAL GROUPS OF THE UNMARRIED ADULT

So far a general picture has been drawn of the sex life of the unmarried adult. In modern society, however, dissimilarities often appear more evident than likenesses. These arise from the complexity of the modern city, the emergence of specialized economic and social types, the freedom of development of individual differences in temperament and personal preference.

It is in these special groups of single persons, such as

hoboes, prostitutes, homosexuals, students, artists, prisoners, soldiers and sailors that the interaction of individual and social factors determining the sex life of the person may, perhaps, be most clearly open to observation and analysis.

Of these groups only three will be briefly analyzed:

(a) The hobo, where sex expression is upon a physical level largely detached from personal, sentimental and cultural elements.

(b) A homosexual, where sex rôles become inverted in the social experience.

(c) The Bohemian, who is living in the present, forgetful of the past, and not vitally concerned for the future.

In *The Hobo,* Nels Anderson portrays realistically the sex life of the migratory homeless man as a resultant of the necessary conditions of his life:

The hobo has few ideal associations with women. Since most of them are unmarried, or living apart from their wives, their sex relations are naturally illicit. The tramp is not a marrying man, though he does enter into free unions with women when the occasion offers. There are many women in the larger cities who have no scruples against living with a man during the winter, or for even a year or two, without insisting upon the marriage rite. They are not prostitutes, not even "kept women."

For most hoboes and tramps the only accessible women are prostitutes and the prostitutes who solicit the patronage of the homeless man are usually forlorn and bedraggled creatures who have not been able to hold out in the fierce competition in higher circles.

All studies indicate that homosexual practices among homeless men are widespread. They are especially prevalent among men on the road among whom there is a tendency to idealize and justify the practice. Homosexuality is not more common among tramps than among other one-sex groups. In the prison and jail population, the authorities are forced to wage a constant warfare against it. The same condition prevails also in the navy or merchant marine, and, to a lesser extent, in the army.

Among tramps there are, it seems, two types of perverts. There are those who are subjects, in the words of Havelock Ellis, "of a congenital predisposition." Most of them are men who have developed from childhood feminine traits and tastes, and they may be regarded as predisposed to homosexuality. The second group is composed of individuals who have temporarily substituted homosexual for heterosexual behavior. Most of these perverts by conversion are men who, under the pressure of sex isolation, have substituted boy for woman as the object of their desires. This is chiefly because boys are accessible, while women are not. The average boy on the road is invariably approached by men who get into his good graces. Some "homos" claim that every boy is a potential homosexual. This is without doubt an exaggeration as well as a defense, for not all boys are subject to persuasion.

In his sex life, as in his whole existence, the homeless man moves in a vicious circle. Debarred from family life, he hungers for intimate associations and affection. The women that he knows, with few exceptions, are repulsive to him. Attractive women live in social worlds infinitely remote from his. The prevalence of sexual perversion among the homeless men is, therefore, but the extreme expression of their unnatural sex life. Homosexual practices arise almost inevitably in similar situations of sex isolation.

The prevailing generally accepted explanations of

homosexuality are either biological or psychoanalytic. The orthodox biological interpretation conceives the true homosexual as the product of inborn tendencies. The psychoanalyst posits homosexuality as an arrest in psycho-sexual development.

To the sociologist, however, homosexuality, as, indeed, heterosexuality, can only be fully understood as cultural phenomena. For the human being, as compared with the animal, sex is a social rôle. From the moment of birth, two divergent lines of expectations, attitudes, and reactions await respectively the boy and the girl.

Consequently, it comes about that one's consciousness of sex, i.e., his masculine or feminine rôle, is as significant as, or more significant than, one's biological sex.

As indicative of this point is an interesting case presented at the 1934 meeting of the American Orthopsychiatric Association. A child who had been mistakenly identified by the midwife as a girl had lived this rôle until fourteen years of age. With the discovery of his biological sex and by transference to a new environment a rapid and successful achievement of the masculine rôle took place.

This case is only an extreme illustration of the well-known fact that with many, if not with most, young children consciousness of the social rôle of sex overshadows, and probably precedes, any effective manifestation of physical or physiological differentiation.

Since sex is a social rôle, the sex status of the individual is determined partly by his conception of himself, and partly by the conception others have of him. It is possible to imagine oneself in the rôle of the other sex or even to identify oneself with it. Quite as powerful are the attitudes and reactions of others to one. Actually, for the determination of both heterosexuality and homosexuality there is constant interaction of one's conception of one's sexual rôle and of the expectations and reactions of others to it. Inversion of rôles may therefore take place in early and later childhood or in adolescence and youth.

Social situations in childhood favoring the emergence of homosexuality in the male are: efforts by the mother to maintain him in the baby rôle; circumstances like illness in childhood predisposing to frailty and sometimes to the acceptance of feminine activities; playing as a child mainly with those of the opposite sex; proficiency in what are regarded as feminine accomplishments. Life histories of many so-called homosexuals provide a background of such childhood experiences, even if the "awakening" in most cases does not occur until introduction into the world of the homosexual at adolescence or youth. Moreover, many cases of apparently true homosexuality seem to show none of these childhood indications, but rather a presence of certain precipitating situations during adolescence and youth. This is typically seen in the process of the creation of the homosexual among hoboes, and in other cases where the inexperienced and innocent are dominated by those already well-versed in homosexual behavior.

The homosexual personality as here defined is to be sharply differentiated from homosexual practices *per se*. The homosexual world, while organized around and by homosexual personalities, includes within it many individuals who are heterosexuals or predominantly heterosexual. It is true that the homosexual world, with its own codes of conduct, its own highly sophisticated and subtle language, and its bizarre events is a potent force in the recruiting of homosexuals. But, on the other hand, it attracts curiosity seekers, sexual adventurers and those who seek in different ways to exploit homosexuals. Some of these may indeed become permanent members of the homosexual world. But the majority seem to remain for a longer or shorter period of experimentation and then return to the world of heterosexuality.

It is from this general sociological standpoint that detailed intensive case studies need to be made of the different types of persons who find their way into the world of homosexuality.

It is in the rooming-house areas of our cities, which harbor the highest proportions of young unmarried adults, that casual, transient and even promiscuous unconventional sex behavior reach their highest frequency and attain the Bohemian sanction of social approval. H. W. Zorbaugh illustrates this in *The Gold Coast and the Slum.*

Such is the world of furnished rooms—a mobile, anonymous, individual world, a world of thwarted wishes, of unsatisfied longings, of constant restlessness; a world in which people, in the effort to live, are building up a body of ideas that free them from a conventional tradition that has become fixed, hard, and oppressive; a world in which individuation, so typical of the life of the city, is carried to the extreme of personal and social disorganization. People behave in strange and incalculable ways; quick and intimate relationships spring up in the most casual way, and dissolve as quickly and as casually.

"I get along fairly well, now. I am no longer lonely. I am surprised to find that I can actually enjoy the girls I pick up at public dance halls, at restaurants, along the lake front, in the park. I know a great many of them now—many of them pretty and clever, and good companions for a night. I no longer go with prostitutes. I soon found that was unnecessary. For the city is full of women who are just as lonely as I was, or who draw on their sex as I would on my bank to pay for the kind of clothes they want to wear, the kind of shows they want to see. Then, too, there are the 'emancipated' women, who don't want to marry, who are not 'gold diggers', but who feel the need of a man and a normal sex life."

Transient but intense personal contacts are characteristic of this "Bohemian" life of "studio" and "tea-room." Combined with the unconventional tradition of the "village," its philosophy of individualism, and the anonymity which its streets afford, these contacts give rise to unconventional types of sex relationship. Moreover, Towertown's debates on free love and its reputation for promiscuity, coupled with its unconventionality and anonymity, attract to its studios many individuals who are not Bohemians, but who seek in Towertown escape from the repressive conventions of the larger community. Many of them become hangers-on of Bohemia, but others isolate themselves in its midst.

The anonymity and unconventionality of "village" streets attracts to them many who merely want to be "let alone." Plenty of individuals do use the anonymity of "village" life, however, to sneak off into holes by themselves. Business and professional men use its studio apartments to keep their mistresses. G—— is a well-to-do lawyer and bachelor and keeps his mistress in the village. There are many such cases, especially of young men, "philistines" through and through, who nevertheless like the *laissez faire* of Bohemia. Distorted forms of sex behavior also find a harbor in the "village." Many homosexuals are among the frequenters of "village" tea-rooms and studios.

The effects of the depression have yet to be studied in their relation to the sex life of the unmarried. Its immediate results are to be seen in decreasing marriages, in an increasing number of unmarried adults, in an increasing illegitimacy, and in the discrimination in relief in favor of married as over against unmarried adults.

More serious and significant for society are the sexual problems of those for whom the depression has meant postponement of marriage. Their predicament and the way that some have taken out of it is forcefully presented by John Hyde Preston in the July issue of *Harper's Magazine* in an article "Love Among the Ruins."

For these young people who are in love in a time of depression there are but three courses open; one must be chosen, although all three entail grave disadvantages. The first course is to deny desire for the time being and follow the way of their parents; the second is to accept desire and live together—that is, cohabit with each other—before marriage; and the third is to marry on what little money they have, swallow their pride, and take a chance on their being able to get along, even if it means having to move in under the family roof for a while.

Either marriage will have to be made easier for young people who are in love among the ruins, or else morals will have to be relaxed even more to meet the exigencies of the present day. Whatever you may think of it on ethical grounds, the fact remains that the majority of young Americans are living together before marriage. They are doing so soberly, with open eyes, and in all solemnity. It is not an experiment, but a need met. It is not a defiance of old standards, but an acceptance of new problems. Yet at best it is only a substitute for marriage, and their hearts and minds are set upon that as the ultimate goal. If it remains as difficult for them as it has been up to this time, then the institution of marriage itself must suffer.

In shelters there are concentrated thousands of detached men, 20,000 last October in Chicago alone, most of them unmarried. Life in the shelter is that of older unmarried men in the mass, secure in lodgings and two meals a day with an abundance of leisure. This special situation affords an unusual opportunity of studying the effect of isolation and severance of normal home and neighborhood ties upon the sex behavior of individuals in the mass. An interesting comparative study might be made of CCC camps where young men are employed under somewhat similar conditions.

A final question remains which will be stated but without attempting an answer. What is the utility or the inutility of the unmarried adult with reference both to his personal development and happiness and to his function in society?

Studies show the great predominance of the single, especially of males, among the criminal, the insane, the physically handicapped and the venereally infected. The higher longevity of the married over the unmarried is well known. These facts are common knowledge but their interpretation is not as simple as might at first appear.

In different societies different solutions are being offered for the problem of the unmarried. In liberal, individualistic countries, like the United States, the unmarried are not recognized as a problem, but being unmarried is a status resulting from the free choice of the individual to marry or not to marry. In Fascist countries, the single state is the object of condemnation, of loss of civil privileges and is a basis for increased taxation. In the Soviet Union, with its low proportion of unmarried, even in the late 'teens and early twenties, sex behavior is considered a private matter, of no public concern unless there are children; and woman, granted full economic equality, is rapidly being freed from domestic duties and emancipated from the centuries of male domination.

The experience of other countries, however, is not likely to point the way to the solution of the sex problems of the unmarried adult in the United States. It is in the American situation and out of the natural course of the evolution of our mores that our sexual and familial patterns will continue to be worked out.

Marriage still remains, and will so continue (assuming favorable conditions) to be the preferred and idealized type of sexual relationship, aspired for and demanded by the overwhelming majority of our young people.

The three conceptions in our American mores that have shaped and will in all probability continue to mold the sexual and familial behavior of our people are:

1. That the highest personal happiness comes from marriage based upon romantic love.

2. That love and marriage are essentially personal and private and are, perhaps, even more than other aspects of life, to be controlled by the individual himself.

3. That, in consequence, sex and marriage are not to

be taken lightly, but seriously, in their import for personal and social welfare.

The lifting of the taboo upon sex discussion, the decline in the value placed upon chastity, the increasing divorce rate, and the trend to companionate marriage, are to be interpreted in the light of a new Puritanism which places its stress not upon the externals of behavior but upon the inner realities of personal relations.

The forecast here made is, in the nature of things, subject to certain conditions. It is assumed that a social revolution will not take place upturning and remolding the mores of the American people. It is also assumed that the New Deal, or a similar program, in keeping with our democratic institutions, will bring about national recovery and normal prosperity.

# ECONOMICS

At the present time two great tendencies are visible in our social organization. On the one hand, the threads of social life are growing closer, and organization, as regards the simple and common means of subsistence, is increasing. On the other hand, as regards the things that most commonly concern the individual person, the sphere of freedom is being perpetually enlarged. . . . The society of the future is a reasonable anarchy founded on a broad basis of Collectivism.—HAVELOCK ELLIS

## THE ECONOMIC BACKGROUND OF THE SEX LIFE OF THE UNMARRIED ADULT

*Mary R. Beard*
EDITOR AND WRITER
ON ECONOMICS

IN THE present American economic interregnum, the relation between the struggle for existence and the sex life of the unmarried adult is a timely question pertinent to social and political development, to ethics, esthetics and statecraft, as well as to human stock and personal happiness. An old economy is passing. A new economy is in the process of becoming. The status and character of unmarried adults within the order-that-is-to-be will mirror the culture of the new age as the status and character of the unmarried adult have reflected the culture of all former ages. The recorded history of human relations early displays concern with the problem of the unmarried and it remains a consideration of prime importance throughout recorded history. Hence the true significance of this timely question lies in its time depth. Its vitality is indicated by its persistence. The dilemma it presents may be resolved, if at all, it would seem, by wisdom gleaned from mankind's total experience with itself, coupled with the will to avoid the repetition of blunders. Fortunately the various forms in which the bodily hungers and their strife for satisfaction have clothed themselves constitute, in time, a fairly open story, although it may not be one which he or she who runs may read.

Unfortunately there has been a tendency in recent years to fix attention on the family, to the exclusion of genuine interest in the mature population that is more or less adrift. For example, a habit has been formed of thinking about women without husbands mainly in terms of sex deprivations and of thinking about men without wives largely in terms of their vocations. This inclination is responsible for the unabashed statement in the United States Census of 1930 that, since "the marital status in relation to occupation is so much more significant in the case of female workers than in the case of male workers," the aforesaid Census restricts its attention to the marital status of females alone. If such was the American mental horizon of 1930, four years later, in 1934, even a statistician could scarcely escape counting undomesticated men, too, for they have a large section of the world by the throat.

The unmarried do not live in social isolation, however their domiciles may be described in mathematical ledgers. Their struggle for existence and the claims which nature makes upon their bodies and minds are not wholly individual affairs; nor can the modern family guard them in every respect if they dwell at home. The unmarried constitute aspects of a total situation which embraces both the economic setting in which they may try to earn their own daily bread or in which their guardians earn it for them and the attendant ideas as well which set for them standards of conduct. That has been true for the unmarried since single blessedness or single woe became conscious of itself or a matter for social observation. Today with untold millions of men and women uprooted from the soil, dismissed from industry, shut out of the professions, footloose, unemployed, resentful of the fate life has meted out to them, but still dynamic and driven forward by irrepressible hungers, the slightest attempt to comprehend their significance, even to themselves, compels consideration of the economic matrix to which they are bound like a composite Prometheus and of the currents of ideas which circulate in the air they breathe.

Throughout the economic background of the generations of unmarried adults who are seeking to solve their personal problems today runs the fact of world depression combined with the ideology of war. Interests and ideas are inseparable partners. Such prosperity as came to America between 1914 and 1929 may be traced largely to her advantage as a manufacturer of arms and as a creditor of nations at war. That prosperity provided work and extraordinary pleasure for American citizens irrespective of their marital status, unless they happened to be ex-soldiers and shell-shocked. But its duration was brief. Within ten years after the World

War the gloom of panic settled down on the American scene.

And the good fortune of America, even on a transient frame, was not shared by nations less fortunately placed in the world economy. Germany, for instance, steadily crumbled into a condition of general misery after the World War. To the humiliation of defeat on battlefields and the failure of war objectives was added economic despair and emotional suffering caused by the breakdown of her domestic industries and credit operations. The experimental republic, liberal in tone and aspiring to a respected place among the nations, possessed neither the material basis for its survival nor the necessary enthusiasm of the populace. In the circumstance, political power went begging in the streets, where it was picked up by soldiers.

The Fascist movement in Germany, as in Italy and Japan, is essentially a dynamic of unmarried males. If strong and desperate men are not helped by the State to sink roots into civilian enterprise and if they cannot do it unaided, they turn invariably to fighting—man's oldest and most enduring trade. The case of Germany is a glaring illustration of the menace to the State inherent in a large citizenry of unoccupied celibates.

Adolph Hitler, a bachelor like the majority of the thirty or forty leaders of the Nazi party, is a rover, a veteran of the World War, undomesticated and unused to the responsibilities connected with public life in a time of peace. He gathered around him in the hour of economic chaos men like himself of sadistic temper, unaffected by the restraining influences which education, jobs, families and public obligations are wont to exert. A number of the prominent Nazis are men with records of sex perversions as well as of military daring.

They were supported in their rise to power by a romantic youth movement, naturally violent, and composed of men just reaching manhood, all poor, all jobless, all energetic, all resentful. These battalions of idle bachelors, with the rage of tigers, leaped over the barriers which civilized nations had erected for human behavior, and hurled themselves upon their prey, snarling and clawing, snatching posts and emoluments from private persons and appropriating state and other property wholesale. The Nazis suggest American gangsters armed with political power. Having seized a State, they reveal the fact that their sole conception of statecraft is that of a bellicose bachelor. The republic, fathered and mothered by democrats, they immediately scrapped. In its place now stands a war machine such as the German State did not represent even under the Prussian Junkers who, as men of family and great estates, regarded war with less light-hearted insouciance than these newcomers into politics who have little to lose by going on a rampage.

The Third Reich is perhaps the first example of a nation dominated by convinced bachelors. In the past, warring males, merely aggressive on foot and on horse, when they were victorious simply seized native women and carried them home to their lairs. The Nazis, on the contrary, are men trained by modern trench warfare, in an isolation from women unknown to a Tamerlane, a Wallenstein or a Pizarro. They are anti-woman in a new sense. They propose to ignore the sex completely. Their case was set forth by Ernst Roehm, as chief of the Storm Troops and Reich Minister without portfolio, the man who organized the Army of the Brown Shirts. In his autobiography (1928) he gave vent to the hostility of the modern veterans toward the opposite sex; he showed how men in the late war were more aloof from women than warriors in former times who marched or rode from town to town altering the racial stock as they passed. To borrow a title from Hemingway, these Nazis are "men without women."

Roehm was a professional soldier in 1908; he served regularly in the World War and then as a soldier of fortune in Bolivia. "I am a soldier," his memoir begins. "I regard the world from my soldierly standpoint, consciously onesided. . . . The aim of my policy is to get German veterans their share in the management of the State. In the coming Reich the Front Fighter shall be respected and privileged above others. . . . Germans have forgotten how to hate. They complain like women instead of hating like men. . . . 'Peace and Order' means softening of the bones. To the Devil with this Peace and Order. . . . If Europe and all the rest of the world sink in flames, what is that to us?"

Roehm never denied the accusations of perversity made in 1932 by the *Welt am Montag,* which published sensational letters of his addressed to boys. His attitude toward the family is revealed in these words, repeating the remark of the wife of one of his Captains: "In the heart of my husband stands in first place his Captain, above whom is nothing; only after that come his mother and myself." And Roehm highly approved this "comradeship of the soldier, cemented by blood" which, he declared, can "never be expunged from the heart."

This rebellion of the undomesticated, un-civil-ized males of contemporary Germany—surplus males—has been accompanied by manifestations indicating the presence of surplus women as well. The first group of women to join Hitler and the Nazis were nationalist and bellicose, a group which had issued a manifesto, just before the Armistice in 1918, demanding that women be called to arms as well as men. As the mothers of Germany were not united in a peace movement, the spinsters, lacking homes and gainful employment themselves in a peace period, reverted wistfully to the "glory" of war which, as Guida Diehl, their leader, says, "took them out of themselves." This need of unmarried women to be "uplifted" by a Cause, even by a holy man, is made painfully clear in Diehl's *Deutsche Frau.*

She calls Hitler a messiah: "In a holy state of divine possession, Hitler serves the mission of God!" She summons women to ally themselves with the messiah and his war band. For their inspiration she offers not the "weak-yielding" Gretchen but "Brunhild, a heroic woman, with whom men must fight" and "Krimhild who takes over the blood-feud and never rests until she has wiped out her whole tribe of kinsmen." Guida Diehl and Hedwig Foerster and other female Nazis mirror the unmarried woman's yearning to forget herself in admiration of weaponed males and in "service" to the "boys" at the front. If bachelors formed the Nazi Party, they were pushed toward power from the very start by women whose votes for Hitler out-number men's in the final reckoning. The craving of these women for homes was frequently laid bare. Hitler explicitly promised this at least: "A good German husband for every good German woman." But the women did not realize, it seems, that they would be marrying German soldiers. Now that they understand, they are increasingly horrified.

The economic interregnum has not come to a violent end in the United States, it is true, and may not end violently. But signals flaming from the pages of the past and world events in the present warrant the gravest assumptions with regard to the effect of economic and emotional hardships on the spirit and designs of mankind. It is generally taken for granted that women lose ground in such circumstances. There may be no exact figures respecting the size of our own unmarried adult population, we may only presume concerning its numbers, we can merely guess at the emotions which sway it. Nevertheless, mindful of the economic setting in which it must function, and aware of the natural impulse for a full life, by all means let us presume.

Before purposes and programs crystallize, alarm bells may be heard ringing from many directions as guides to thought and action for the American order-that-is-to-be. Note the hordes of young men and women wandering about the continent, like nomads, in search of sustenance and comfort, as the aborigines were doing when the Europeans arrived on the scene in the 17th century. This 20th century migration of homeless, tool-less and landless persons bears no resemblance to the activity and optimism which settled and exploited the continental domain. Older generations carried cattle and plows with them, staked out claims upon public lands and carved out states for a nation. This generation of rovers looks forward to no independence, individual or familial. Its highest reach in hopefulness is the winning of a chance to labor for someone already established, secure, and in need of employees. If the vigor of these Americans gone nomad is praiseworthy and their initiative commendable, if, in other words, they refuse simply to squat beside closed mills and mines, offices and shops, in the event that their quest for work proves futile, their very determination not to be utterly defeated may sweep them into the party of any magnetic personality, however demagogic, who offers them a program. The risks of a national relapse into banditry and savagery may be minimized. Dillinger lived as a lone Robin Hood and his moll an isolated Harpalyce, but it is surely well to remember how thin is the veneer which civilization spreads over mankind's natural urges.

"What is the source of this man's rage? Of this woman's fury?" asks an outstanding columnist. And no query is more important. Resentment at society, coupled with the economic chaos which provides exercise for malcontents, is the source material of every known dictatorship. Unemployment, every investigator nowadays reports, is an unmistakable compulsion to crime. Knowing this, the War Department has made full preparation for handling "eventualities," in the form of organized rebellion, by its own expertly organized and well-equipped force. And not only does the present Secretary of War, George H. Dern, call for a strengthened standing army but in that plea he is joined by an ex-secretary of War, Newton D. Baker, who felt assured while he was in office that not even for America did the World War end in 1918. While the Treaty of Versailles was being penned, he was insisting that the United States must take more lads into its army. All men and innumerable women think in terms of rioting and fighting. Can they think in any other terms?

The signs and symbols of social havoc inherent in economic chaos shoulder up in other ways above the plane surface view of peace and order lightly held by the complacent. They appear in the resurgence of prostitution, open and clandestine, in the cities; in the dearth of positions awaiting college graduates and the steady sinking down of the white-collar classes into the ranks of the proletariat, or, lower, into the ranks of the paupers. They are evident in the bankruptcy of trust funds set aside for the care of the "well-born"; in the weakened capacity of parents to provide for their daughters that ancient and long-enduring encouragement to matrimony, the "dot"; in the sex segregation attending efforts to relieve the needy when the unmarried are being succored; the comparative neglect of single persons in schemes for charitable or work assistance. They are manifest in the wretched hovels where "hoboes" foregather; in the free-loving of the free; in the raids on the national treasury by veterans of the late war; in the hunger marches on the Capital; in the closure of opportunities for mature individuals with experience and capacity to apply their knowledge and talents in public life. They are mirrored in the mounting insanity and suicides; in the community efforts to amuse the forlorn that they may be at least mentally occupied; in the increasing number of clinics for the psychopathic; in the propaganda among the well-circumstanced for the sterilization of the "unfit"; in the assemblies of the young debating ways out of youth's tragedy; and in the violent solutions offered for this riddle of the universe —bread and a full life for all.

No picture of a civilized society ever conceived by the mind of man or woman would tolerate in any particular this starvation of brawn and brain, this narrow channeling of the human spirit, this confinement of thought and action, this peril to human stock, this menace to a democratic republic erected in a New World in an age of abundance and still faced with the potentialities of plenty. Men and women cannot be made social outcasts with impunity—to themselves or to the commonweal. Yet the number of pariahs in the United States at this hour mounts to uncalculated millions. Their interest lies in economic security and a rounded personality. The dominant idea in their times is violence. Interests and ideas flow together.

When we consider the problem of celibacy and the State, we must consider how often the European nations have been wrecked by unmarried hordes. The conclusion seems inescapable that, if husbands and maternity are essential to women's mental health, paternity and wives are as vital to that of the males. The rulers of societies in the Far East in days gone by connected marriage and political stability as an inseparable affair. The family system was deliberately linked to statecraft. As early as the 6th century B.C., Confucius prescribed the family system as a remedy for the feudal anarchy of China, and monarchs adopted this philosophy in order to consolidate their centralized power. Thus when the Japanese shoguns took over Confucianism in the 17th century, A.D., it was with the conscious determination to base the State on the family. And today the unique national cohesion of the Japanese is in a striking measure due to the Shinto (the national religion) emphasis on the family. In ancient India, too, although Buddha taught celibacy, he had first tried marriage, and the Hindus still marry extremely early. Not until their full maturity, after their families are founded, do the men feel justified in entering holy orders.

This exaltation of the family has never proceeded so far in the Occident. While Church and State united to consecrate marriage, the feudal economics defeated marriage on a vast scale, for the eldest son inherited the family estate and the younger sons were obliged to enter the Army or the Church. Europe was continuously filled with restless throngs of unmarried adults, footloose as well as family-loose. They provoked much of the turmoil as well as much of the progress in the West. Thus the old French monarchy was led to economic ruin partly through its effort to finance the vast aggregation of religious celibates in its midst. Many revolutions occurred as the consequence of revolts by the married against the claims of the unmarried for support. The separation of Church and State in France eventually reflected this dispute.

Slavery, war and prostitution absorbed their share of the responsibility for surplus men and women, and effected a gigantic combination, in fact, for carrying out the task. Indeed, this alliance remains active in Japan, where hapless youths serve Mars and hapless girls serve Venus, the latter generally sold in childhood to the brothels. In Germany the new social prescription reads that no damsel must divert a soldier from his course of "raw brutalism" through the agency of feminine wiles. Prostitution is *de rigeur,* with emphasis on the rigor. But if ethical perceptions are equally lacking in Japan under a revived State-as-War, esthetics holds a tighter rein. In Japan even the warrior is expected to take his sexual pleasure with artistic delight. The military officer of the Japanese race is apt to be a poet. He has been trained in the appreciation of art. He enjoys music and he esteems dainty food. Not so long ago he actually drank his tea ritualistically. His one true god is a female—the Sun Goddess—ancestor of his race, a benign agricultural deity, chiefly disturbed because her brother's piebald colts have been allowed to ramp over her rice fields. In her distress the goddess retreated to a cave but she was lured forth again to bless mankind through the medium of the dance. She is thus no Brunhild, no Teuton deity wrecking even her kinsmen in her fury. She is a genial creature permitting human graces. And the geisha girl, with her religious affiliations, is noted for her graces—her posturing, singing, dancing and elegant costuming. Since interests and ideas move along in a united front, possibly their feministic religion stamps sex manners on the Japanese. At any rate, the sexual slave is an adjunct of Japanese politics and a conspicuous feature of every new community which the race establishes in the world.

Baroness Shidzuè Ishimoto would check the supply of prostitutes at its source by birth control, but, while that movement makes some headway, the enormous birth rate meanwhile makes the mass production of sexual slaves so preposterous that all the politicians can devise are schemes for migration and imperialism.

The sing-song girls of China and the nautch girls of India are more manifestations of the economic alliance—slavery, war and prostitution. Infanticide was the more primitive way of balancing mouths and the food supply, and infanticide is not unknown nowadays in China. It lingered in the highly sophisticated Greek societies beside prostitution, as a means of handling overpopulation and at that stage of birth control knowledge, Plato was unable to eliminate it from his social planning. Greece, however, contributed high ethical values to thought about life. Granted that she erected free-loving into a cult of beauty worship, her courtesans served as models for immortal works of art. Granted that the discipline in singing, playing on musical instruments, dancing and "teasing" required of the Greek hetairae of the better sort was as exacting in all probability as that demanded of the Japanese geisha in our time, nevertheless the gold-digging propensities of the fairest courtesans worried the elder statesmen of Athens who knew that the prowess of the State on land and sea was contingent on its material resources. For State revenue, the rigorous ordering of private property was imperative. What was spent on mistresses, especially on foreign women, was often so much lost for the State; hence the war side of the aforesaid alliance clamored for more weight in its balance of power as against slavery and prostitution. And there was another item in its accounting induced by the reluctance of both sexes to marry. If the family was to lay the foundation of political stability, then philandering must be relegated to the status of a social evil, and so it was by the founding fathers of the Greek states. They made the costs of non-marital liberties as high as possible. And even Sappho, lyrical over romantic love, was materialistically alarmed because her brother was squandering his fortune on a mistress. She addressed no erotic verse to the young slave girl whom he bought and enriched.

Reformers, however, who sought to revise custom, at once confronted the religious fundamentalists, who could prove that their ways were the ways of the gods. Thus the very bible of the Greeks, Homer, encouraged wantonness. The frank homosexuality among the Greeks had for its pattern the story of Ganymede, and mortals were known to "adorn their chambers with paintings of their gods in positions of unnatural lust," and to engrave them so on seal rings. Sophocles entitled one of his plays "The Lovers of Achilles." Young maidens assembled in schools of poetry where they expressed their personalities in amorous verse to the imaginative limit. And was not the guardian angel of Athens and of other Greek States a Virgin? Through conversations with a priestess, Diotima, Socrates averred that he got ideas about romantic love. Economically cramped by narrow territory and overpopulation, dominated by slavery and caste arrangements which relegated all manual labor, including that associated with the fine arts, to slaves or the "low-born," the opportunities available to the well-born Greeks for trying their wings were exceedingly restricted. Hence their contribution to culture and to civilization was made from necessity in what Aristophanes ridiculed as the "think shop." The Greek philosophers represented a "brain trust." But teaching while thinking developed into a lauded profession, intellectually endowed by the practical experiences with life which veterans of the ancient wars brought to the vocation. Socrates, Plato and Aristotle had all been soldiers and their ideas were grounded on realities. They are known as rationalist philosophers. Æschylus, the first great playwright, was likewise a veteran; he directed the attention of playgoers to the hardships which war brought on non-combatants.

Through companionate liaisons with thoughtful men, unmarried Greek women perhaps more than wives extended the reaches of intellectualism. Single women had the run of the Greek islands. They possessed keen minds. They had wit as well as curiosity. They were members of all the academies and, indeed, were heads of some. The roots of the Stoic religion which finally mastered Rome may be unearthed in Megara, where the teacher of Zeno, founder of Stoicism, studied under the woman, Euklides.

With the loss of Greek independence, the mighty Alexandrian empire furnished new and broader outlets for the energies of the Greeks. Talents, hitherto held in leash or directed into specific channels by economic conditions, tribal customs and codes of honor, broke their bonds; and not only politicians, warriors and teachers now found exercise for their genius but room was given to inventors, explorers, researchers, travelers, builders and engineers, manufacturers and merchants on an unheard-of scale. Women then won the right to play female rôles in the theater, a privilege preëmpted by men in old Greece. If the mime, as she was called, still earned her sustenance through sex appeal, she at least acquired a status of semi-economic independence. Book-making developed as an accredited occupation for the two sexes. There was new work and plenty of it for Greek men and women, married and single, in bearing their culture far and wide under the patronage of the doughty Alexander.

From the Greek cultural magnet which so attracted Alexander, Cato the Elder tried to hold the Romans aloof, especially from the influence of the Greek female. But it was Roman destiny to distribute Greek culture even further afield than Alexander had done. While unmarried Roman males joined married men in the wars for empire, a new profession appeared for men in Rome, a civilian pursuit known as the law, and it became an obsession rivaling sex and pugilism. While young children, especially girls, continued to be exposed to death or slavery, unmarried women, surplus women, Roman as well as Greek, rose to prominence in the professions of medicine and nursing, acting, teaching, painting and merchandising, among others. Sex was thus repressed by public interests and ideas, by opportunities to earn a livelihood in unwonted ways, and by more wilful spending as wants enlarged or multiplied.

But such liberties collapsed with imperialist enterprise. And in this crisis the cult of celibacy swept all else before it. Distraught by political and social calamities, amid physical dangers more imminent because of the depletion of Roman defenders and the barbarian invasions, the Romans turned in their defeatism to self-perfection as a dominating ideal—to a modified Stoicism which counted on rewards after death for spiritual martyrdom. If Roman males started the ball rolling toward asceticism, the females certainly pushed it fast and accumulatively. The first organizing funds for a Christian Church flowed into the coffers of the priests from the chests of Roman heiresses. Rich matrons, with their daughters, granddaughters and daughters' friends, transformed their huge unproductive estates in Europe and Africa into productive piety. They founded monasteries and went to live within their walls. They bought new lands and built asylums for celibates upon them. Brothers and sisters diverted their holdings to similar purposes, and husbands in enormous numbers, too, were forced to revert to chastity. Courtesans did penance and buried themselves in retreats.

That the rigid doctrine of virginity made such growth among the Romans was due in part to the propaganda against intermarriage with Teutons and to the desire to preserve Roman blood from barbaric contamination. Monks were succeeding so well in capitalizing the despair of women, surplus women, perhaps, as the end of Roman independence seemed imminent, by instilling among them the desire for a mystic marriage with Christ, that a pagan emperor, Valentinian I, tried to keep the celibates away from ladies' palaces. But he was too late with his prohibitive ukase. To women's lavish endowment of the Church and the Church Fathers, and their ardor for its ascetic direction, may be traced in generous measure its triumph and its bent. Women pleaded for and financed the withdrawal of Roman citizens from the politics of State to the politics of religion. As Greek women before their time had participated in the erection of systems of rationalist philosophy, Roman women now shared in the heated factional disputes through which schools of religious zealots battled for dominance. Women lured to the Christian cult such uncompromising interpreters of the struggle for existence and sex as the passionate and wayward Augustine; it was with a sigh of relief that his Christian mother, Monica, saw the gates of a retreat close behind her perverse offspring; and if he strode upstage behind its walls with his thesis that women are the root of all evil, his own mother previously had considered them so in relation to his career.

Virgins helped matrons to create the ideology of sex as sin and the celibate practices of the long monastic era. In so doing they were heiresses not only to Roman wealth but of Roman devotion to the phenomenon of sex—the core of the varied cults that one after the other inundated the Eternal City. Their grip was not relaxed by the Christian monastic movement, for the consciousness of awe, pain, gratitude, hunger, penitence, hope, love and mercy still found no satisfactory application that did not involve sex.

Monasticism, however, was varied in its offerings to the unmarried. Through the priesthood, males escaped military service under barbarians. They likewise escaped family duties without having to be total abstainers in the matter of female society. Could they not lecture the ladies to their hearts' content, consult with them, pray with them, hear their confessions, and be as fathers and brothers to them? Be their holy men? If single blessedness had its price, though it was increasingly the purpose of the Papacy to prevent family interests from penetrating into the monasteries so that the whole attention and revenue of these institutions might serve the interests of the Vatican, though the celibates of both sexes had to serve the Church materialistically, yet monks and nuns achieved economic security in the form of food, clothing and shelter as well as protection from military service in a turbulent age, and by asceticism simple folk could reach powerful offices. In some retreats they had to labor strenuously with their hands and earn this security in the sweat of their brow, but they had access to the soil and their manual labor was placed on grounds deemed estimable for any class. As for the terrible urgency of sexual love, "the timeless ingredient of life," that they did their best to sublimate in the worship of a statue to the Virgin, their little shrines to the Madonna defying every papal ban. Even so, nature enforced her demands and the illegitimate children of holy men mounted to shocking numbers in the environs of the retreats. Nor was the communication between monks and nuns entirely on a puritanic basis, as the reports of supervising bishops disclose. When seclusion grew too gruelling, there was a possible escape to missionary fields with the wide, wide world as the arena.

While monasticism provided for Roman women a flight from financial panic and mental bewilderment to sheer ecstasy, no doubt, it was also a spring into freedom in many ways. Thus learned converts took charge of the Dalmatian monk, Jerome, and set him to composing a version of the Bible for the West. With respect to Frankish, Germanic and Anglo-Saxon Sisters, unusual avenues to liberty and power opened through their retirement from courts to celibacy. Parenthetically, one might insert the fact that Buddhism also furnished something in the way of a shield for Oriental activism. Thus Masako, widow of the shogun Yoritomo, ruled the State after his death with a strong hand by virtue of membership in a holy order which she joined. As the "nun-shogun" she was exempt from the repressions governing ordinary females.

For five or six centuries after the collapse of the Roman Empire the energies of celibates went into pioneering on a tremendous program. Thus they claimed the forests of Germany and Britain for civilization. Monks and nuns went forth to found towns, for example, Bremen, and to carry books to the Irish bogs; they conquered the wilderness and baptized the heathen. For many a generation, as Dopsch shows, religious celibacy had an activist motive *par excellence*, reaching around the globe with its enterprise.

By turning from conquest through marriage to direct conquest over land, English noblewomen attained an economic independence of feudal proportions and a freedom to dare and to do which court life would only have hampered. One recalls, for example, Hild, Abbess of Whitby, a pioneer in this Northern woman movement, a feudal lord managing a joint community of men and women celibates who worked and lived on her domain, and, in addition, a forceful teacher-propagandist who trained some five bishops to carry far and wide the gospel of feudal religiosity. The nuns were not always confined behind their convent walls by any means. They, too, roamed on occasion. They made trips to see the Pope. They attended religious synods. They visited courts. They journeyed over the continent of Europe on political no less than religious errands. Before them, laymen and laywomen bent the knee, metaphorically speaking, and into their exchequers poured gifts from wives and husbands ostensibly devoted to the family. Certain orders of nuns were severely criticized by the Church Fathers for their love of fine plumage; it would have been deemed better to enrich Mother Church. Others, renouncing frivolities, led the very Papacy forward into charitable undertakings, making social work one of the main assets of the Church in its contest with temporal rulers.

The Crusades represented a mass movement of devout celibates, in addition to an excursion of married men and female hangers-on. But one must not forget the fighting orders of knights—*Ritterorden*—which held back the Slav waves from overwhelming Prussia and, indeed, the whole of Europe. One of these orders, the Knights Templar, was supposed to have been more inclined than the others to tolerate perversity, symbolized, it is maintained, in the order's heraldic bearing—two men on one horse. So in our own historical moment, a new Nazi professor at Berlin University, Alfred Baeumler, is one among many men working at a celibate philosophy for the Third Reich. He declares that the military State cannot be founded on the family but only on the close association of men and boys. "Not the home and salon, but the male-assembly and the field-camp are the symbolic realities." He makes exceedingly plain what scores of writers are saying, namely that the Prussian State, with its heritage from the medieval *Ritterorden,* is akin to the ancient Greek State—military and male. The Nazis have chosen for their bard the poet, Stefan Georg, who hymns the love of man for man.

British knights were famed as slayers of dragons and for removing the terrors of the frontier in other ways. Thus Mallory's *Morte d'Arthur* is a long bachelor pæan. Those who marry, as one of the knights says, lose interest in dragons and tournaments. And, of course, the Holy Grail is found only by the pure and perfect Galahad. But to the Germans, Galahad is ridiculous.

Guilds of laymen and their wives, as time advanced, took control of commodity production and the market in which goods were sold. Then the ascetics, once able to find release for their emotional vitality by hard labor on the soil, through their handicrafts, processions and singing, by fasting and praying, with their brushes and quills, were thrown back upon meditation more and more. In their plight, mysticism captured monasticism, visions supplanted toil and prophets and prophetesses appeared as the sensational phenomena of changed economic operations.

In the 15th century three attacks were made on celibacy, though not all three wittingly. One was caused by Jeanne d'Arc, who heard voices calling her outside the convent walls and who dramatically raised temporal politics in France to a post of importance and power hitherto held by the Church. Another was due to the monk, Martin Luther, in coöperation with the nun, Catherine von Bora, who launched the Protestant Revolution and thus directed wider attention from the politics of religion to the religion of politics—that is, to the State. Marrying, these two dramatized the family as the foundation of the State. The third attack came when Columbus paved the way for sea power and revealed the potentialities of silver and gold.

Luther proposed to solve the celibate problem of Europe by marriage. But Columbus, unknown to him, had found another way to dispose of surplus energies. The discovery of America opened a fresh theatre in which unmarried adults could play their various rôles. The 16th century witnessed their ardent exploration and marauding expeditions into distant realms while women stayed at home pursuing the arts of industry and peace. In the 17th century there was work for surplus males in battling over the discovered lands and in carving out new territories. In the 18th century further occupation was furnished in contending for the markets that were developed in the territories. For three centuries, therefore, no compulsion to settle down to a domestic life and civic duties was felt by the surplus men. Sometimes accompanied by their raggletaggle women, the armies of *Landsknechte* swarmed like locusts over the Continent of Europe looking for sustenance while, on the sea, multitudes of males perished fighting.

And when all was as a tale that is told, by the 19th century, when the last blood-letting directed by Napoleon had temporarily settled the celibate problem, a new solution loomed—the mechanical. The Industrial Revolution was on the calendar of history. In Japan, as in England and the United States, the early stages of the Industrial Revolution were marked by a kind of industrial monasticism. It was in the secular retreats of a machine age that this latest phase appeared. Girl workers in the textile factories were housed in company dormitories and a watch and ward was kept on their liberty of movement. But this scheme did not last. Profiteering potentialities reduced the plant owners' anxiety about their personnel; nor did the working women long accept their jails. Only in the detail of wages did sex retain much identity with labor; women were regularly paid less than men.

To retrieve the merest vestige of their former recognition as human beings, which was their lot under the old household economy, or to go forward into a day of such regard, women working away from home sometimes had to fight with the strike as their aggressive weapon. Thus, romanticism about the machine economy died away. It was understood in its stark reality—not as public service but as service to profiteers. Unmarried adults of both sexes who were gainfully employed toiled for money rewards—not for direct consumption of the things they produced. Pleasure was thus an affair of good fortune; it was no longer an affair of creative labor. Everyone in need—and that meant more than ten million women alone, in 1930, in the United States—was out in the big world as an individual at work, and unless he or she could combine with his fellows and bargain collectively, he or she was operating according to a philosophy of grab-as-grab-can. Humanity was moving back to a primitive tooth-and-claw mode of life and labor.

In this titanic upheaval in household economy and its attendant mood, the path to the future had been blazed by men. They invented the machines. They assumed sole direction of industry. The interests and ideas attached to the industrial revolution were distinctly masculine for some time. Women were far from alert in giving the new economy objectives and in setting its patterns of thought. They were more lethargic than their forebears had been in helping to guide the monastic scheme of economy. It is true that in the 17th century Mary Astell was mindful of the threat to family women implicit in the coming of inventions, and in her alarm the modern feminist movement may be said to have had its rise. But there were two intervening centuries before a great organized woman movement took a conscious share in the making of a new philosophy and a new system of labor.

On account of the minute divisions of labor induced

by machine invention and the broadening opportunities for gainful employment which went with this division, the family lost the attraction won for it by the Protestant Reformation, regardless of whatever thought was still expended by moralists in an effort to uphold its priority. Since a man now had to support his wife and children, in most cases solely by his wages or his salary, marriage was oftener out of the question than it had been in the days when direct access to the land and raw materials made living secure if not magnificent. Since, whichever one's sex, one now had to devote a tedious and concentrated apprenticeship in a fiercely competitive trade or profession if one aspired to the higher monetary rewards, marriage was delayed for a large sector of the gainfully employed upper class. This was wholesome as a check on the birth rate—birth-control knowledge being in its infancy—a gain for the development of formal learning and scholarship of the more sterile sort, a social asset owing to the fact that competence in enterprises requiring special skills was best served by this means, and a contribution to humanism because social work again received the steadfast and unalloyed devotion of ascetics. Plato had esteemed late marriages best for the State regarded as Utopia. He thought that human stock would be improved by this prolongation of infancy. And to such notions of the proprieties must be added in our time the public claim to its money's worth from the individuals which it has itself educated. Being interest-on-capital-investment-minded, the investing public desires not vague cultural attainments from its beneficiaries but positive dividends for itself.

Under the capitalist economy, occupation for both sexes ranged from a central type where work and a complete life were intimately related, as they had been in the preceding household economy, to a distant periphery where they bore no relation at all and where every degree of sublimation was necessitated for the maintenance of working efficiency. The changes of the 20th century alone may be observed in this respect. For example, in 1900, in *How Women May Earn a Living,* Helen Church Candee wrote as follows: "As long ago as 1840, when Ferraro was the fashionable dancing-master of New York, he had as assistant his graceful wife, who, with her slim ankles exposed to the interested gaze of the pupils, instructed the gilded youth of the day to dance. In these latter days we hear of women who make dancing a means of earning money, if not for actual support, at least a sum which ekes out a small income. And so the teaching of dancing must be counted as one of the employments open to women." The surprised lifting of a ladylike author's brow is observable as she identifies work and sex, as if a new economic deal had come to unmarried women. And in a sense she was entitled to be surprised, for with the sweep of the industrial revolution in a Puritan climate of taste and opinion, the identification was not always made. Nevertheless, side by side with the relatively restrained teacher of dancing, working in the upper social strata, another woman, the woman of the underworld, danced and appealed to her especial set, along lines of labor and life created in the days of Alexander and earlier.

Feminism, the woman movement of a capitalist economy, began in 1848 to raise its banner of the "perfect good" in terms of gainful employment and property rights. Thus exulted Mrs. Jennie June Croly, a leader in this direction of a later time distinguished for her share in organizing her sex for a world of changing thought: "Poverty of work is the worst form of poverty." That, no doubt, it had always been because it spelled destitution. But Mrs. Croly went on to say: "Work takes us out of ourselves as marriage does not." Obviously work and marriage had been divorced. Sex parasitism had reached the family, as Olive Schreiner eloquently argued. With the experience of wives to urge them on, unmarried women readily magnified labor into a virtue *per se*. Charges of uxoriousness, contemptuously hurled at the happily married, oftentimes acted as the defense mechanism for the unhappily unmarried to whom work was not completely satisfying. On the other hand, the wives were apt to counter with insinuations about the "Third Sex," not always mindful in their turn of the material needs of the unmarried. By dictatorial decree in Fascist Germany this battle of the ladies is temporarily hushed, with housewives more or less applauding, but in the time depth which is the history of the future, as well as of the past, it can hardly be forever terminated by political ukase.

Ideas of sexual liberty changed with the character of the struggle for existence. Concepts of value altered. Whereas in the age of monastic philosophy, illegitimate children were a shame to be concealed by their fathers and as far as might be by their mothers, they were frequently dropped into a basket for foundling lowered for that purpose from the window of a convent by protective Sisters of Charity who saved the babies for Mother Church. Today in the age of secular moralities, a woman in a business or profession may have a child without a wedding, secure its maintenance by the father according to law without his personal coöperation in its rearing, and, indeed, receive a pension from the State for its support if the father cannot be made responsible. A woman can be still freer—that is, she can have a "laboratory baby" and never know its father herself. In this case the unmarried male may be both a parent devoid of domestic obligations and an individual absolved from "sin." Admitting that this is a rare and exaggerated species of functional liberty, its excuse, if it has one, is the hostility displayed toward married women employees by the trades and professions in which they must toil. Women teachers, in particular, face barriers to marriage, as though the public which pays for their education demands of them their last sacrifice. Commercial extortions supplement educational exactions, requiring one hundred per cent loyalty to profits. Having become heretical about profits, Russia is also lenient toward its women with respect to marital rights.

While the conscientious and ambitious woman strives to fix her attention as closely as may be on her work and to derive her satisfaction by trade or professional achievement, the more volatile and perhaps the less gifted woman is sadly immune to the facts of low wages, bad conditions of labor and the absence of opportunity for advancement. This type of unmarried adult waits for a miracle to happen. She expects marriage eventually to lift her out of her struggle for existence on its lonely plane. She does not accept the dogma that work gives more satisfaction than wedlock. And yet marriage under modern economics rarely solves her problem of want and rarely proves a substitute for hard labor, whatever solace it may bring to the soul. For this reason the women who work casually in contemporary mills and shops and offices, while they watch for Princes Charming to take them home, become a difficult community problem. "In an exclusive sense," says Elizabeth Butler in a survey of the scene in Pittsburgh, "these women made up a new labor force such as employers of an earlier generation would not have hired, for they had not the instruments to use it economically; nor would they have had social sanction for doing so. . . . The articulation of this group of human beings to the processes, buildings, tools, wages, hours and health environment of modern industrial plants, becomes a matter charged with importance far beyond the numerical strength of wage-earning women." It is these women especially who stand at the edge of the abyss into which the Western sexual proletariat has fallen.

It cannot be denied, however, that the unmarried who do not look to magic power in a wedding ring and who may be able to put marriage out of their plans can also be community problems. Just as the gilded youth of proud Athens raised social issues by their flair for sex perversions, so today homosexuality returns to vex society, whose interest lies in the normal functioning of fine human stock no less than in an orderly distribution of wealth and its diversion to the State for public ends. With this tendency to abnormalities, the upper classes are inclined to degenerate, together with the rougher soldiery.

But degeneration is less insistent for the general civilian. There were never before so many modes as the present civilized societies offer for sublimating sex. Vows of poverty and penance for natural hungers and delights are as outmoded as Protestant Puritanism. But they still exist. How grown-ups spend is determined solely by their incomes and their tastes. Women's fancies are responsible for the enormous expansion of what may be called the sex industries—cosmetics, lingerie, perfumes, jewels, gowns, and beauty parlors. Countless employers, however, share this responsibility by their preference for employees thus adorned. How men spend is less flamboyantly a sex phenomenon. Indeed, there is scarcely any scheme which men have concocted for forgetting sex which women do not also make their own, even the prize-fight luring them to its environs. Motor cars, airplanes, houses and gardens, exploration, travel, missionizing, propagandizing, organizing, lecturing, music and art, letters, public service, politics, all the businesses, professions and pleasures are alike open to both sexes in all the surviving liberal countries. Sex discrimination in such lands lies in the comparative incomes, the numbers of men and women doing this or that, and in the types of spending which individuals prefer.

Such is the modern economic struggle and such the vagaries of sex, theoretical and customary. But both assume industry and finance capitalism in full swing. The truth is that that swing has become a good deal like a full stop. With millions of Americans on poor relief, wards of private citizens or of the government, and more millions presumably in want, of whom no precise knowledge is to be had, the age-old horror of overpopulation (despite mass production, and notwithstanding the acceptance of the creed that the individual is a privileged person), lifts its hoary head defying the modern age to bury it permanently.

In this crisis the cry grows stronger in America, as around the world, for the conventional escape from public calamity—more war. The potentialities of peace in a technological time demand for their realization the play of social, constructive talents—brains, in short—which mankind has been slower to develop than the cruel, destructive skills. Rather than sink disgracefully down into a pauper's grave, surplus men tend to revert to the rigid concepts of heroism that they may at least perish glamorously. And young women, impressed by the futilities of their lives, dally with the idea that war offers glory for them, too.

Amid such economic conditions and such mental bewilderment, facing such passions and such dire needs, explorations are being made by the rational into ways and means of abolishing the raw brutalism of war as an answer to the riddle of the universe, particularly in view of the fact that war seems to settle nothing. Up and down the long corridors of office buildings in Washington, the capital of the American Republic, move today intelligent young men and women by the thousands, bent on errands of economic mercy for married and unmarried alike. They are devoting the maximum of their physical and mental energy to the task of solving, not mystically, not sadistically, but realistically and sensibly, the economic problems of this latest age. A secular philosophy competent to the new economic deal conceivably may be achieved in these corridors of time.

# MEDICINE

To marry for hygienic reasons is often the same as to drown oneself to satiate thirst.
—PAOLO MANTEGAZZA

## MEDICAL REFLECTIONS UPON SOME LIFE HISTORIES

*Robert L. Dickinson, M.D.*
HONORARY SECRETARY OF THE
NATIONAL COMMITTEE ON
MATERNAL HEALTH

THE CHANGES in attitudes on sex behavior, as may be noted by any physician who studies his office histories of five, or even two, decades, appear to have been gradual at first, then accelerated and radical. To the medical man or woman belongs one of the important methods of approach to the sex problems of the unmarried adult. The main approach involves an analysis of a large series of written or oral reports such as those made by Davis, Kopp, Malamud or Strakosch, or by an intensive questioning of a small series, as compiled by Hamilton. It is noteworthy that the publication of such analyses dates back only ten years and that it constitutes the earliest systematic evaluation in detail of valid evidence of sex behavior—the Freudian being very fragmentary. The medical approach, if well planned, supplements a verbal history of the findings at general physical examination, and through mental tests and studies of hormone endowment and activity, also, by correlating the verbal statement with the objective evidence furnished by genital anatomy.

Alterations in present-day attitudes and in conditions seem to reveal certain leading characteristics, although we may be temporally too close to them to interpret them in proper perspective. These include:

1. Experimentation on the part of more than one nation and by numberless individuals.

2. Frankness and open-mindedness in discussion—or the beginnings thereof.

3. Removal or lessening of penalties, physical and social.

This appears to me the main grouping of the factors: to wit, trial and error; straight talk; birth control. These three. And the greatest of these is birth control.

As far as erotic satisfactions are concerned, there are alternate ways of trying to determine whether new circumstances have brought, or promise to bring, new values. They might be labeled, the one, trial, the other, denial. The first is the prolonged follow-up of actual experience in the endeavor to determine whether a large measure of freedom is feasible without loss of the best values in life and love, or, in other words, whether human nature can be trusted in a fashion or degree to which we have never been willing to trust it. The second is the method of continuing to hunt reasons for placing erotic play and pleasure in a condemned class by itself, and of seeking arguments for exalting asceticism in sex life as the only high-minded principle—a principle, be it noted, thus applied in our day to one department of living and to one alone.

The first inquiry seeks to learn whether or not erotic artistry—now that it is freed or soon to be freed from physical penalty—is one of the functions of the body-and-spirit which can be developed and enjoyed, as we enjoy music and art and out-door exercise. Its motive is a search into the possibilities of simplified happiness, as well as of wide and high emprise, under two provisos: namely, that sexual gratification be delivered from the old inhibitions which have made every one of its manifestations tainted and suspect, and also that full consideration for others be always in mind.

The doctor has his own place as a witness to the development of immunity from physical penalty for erotic activity, moreover, he can watch the effect of such immunity on mind and soul. His contribution can be considerable if he has the special qualifications which secure the confidence of the gentle half of the race and the less articulate confidence of the cruder half. He thus may be in a position to testify to the lessening of anatomical virginity with, however, an increasing essential chastity.

There was entire logic in the old moralistic medical stand. Any completed sex act might end in disaster or a lifelong obligation, such as a child or a marriage. Any sex play whatever might incite to the complete sex act, hence an all-inclusive condemnation of sex intercourse, together with every incentive or preliminary or even any substitute for it. The only exception wholly approved was intercourse deliberately undertaken to start a new life, say ten to twenty times in the average twenty-five years of marriage. When such doctrine prevailed there was logic in the degradation of the sex organs as shame organs and disgust centers. Hence there was need to hide the genitals. Nakedness implied nastiness. Sex was anathema. The really pure in heart, the nun, washed under her robe, without exposure of an inch of skin.

Present terror at the new status is likewise logical. The moment the sex act becomes immune to ancient hazards, protected from sequels of venereal suffering and long obligation, the door opens wide to the possibilities of its being merely another form of a contribution to happiness. Venus was not unknown to Epicurus. With the disappearance or alleviation of serious physical consequences, will the moral mischief-cloaking sexuality shrink? After all need of deception and hypocrisy is gone, will harm to character no longer result from sex play within the bounds of good taste and thoughtfulness for others? Dare we even ask these questions? Dare we gather examples?

What becomes of the teaching that venereal diseases and illegitimacy were invented by God to frighten us away from sexual pleasures? What of the thunder of a conspicuous early Father of the Church that the race might better perish from the earth than be perpetuated by so foul a process? One is impelled to ask what would happen to the dwellers in the tropics if their clothes and their food fell under regulation by the Esquimaux in the way that marriage control is assumed by the monastery or the monastic minded? One might hide behind Latin and declare, *non compos testis, non compos mentis.* One might think other comparisons warranted. A eunuch may rule a harem for a sultan but shall a theologian who elects to be a mental castrate continue to arrogate to himself the laying down, in elaborate detail, of laws for techniques of love for a people? Shall the canons of art be laid down by the blind, the laws of harmony by the deaf; mathematics be ruled by emotions; physiology by theology?

If an alteration in belief is under way, the explanation may lie in the removal or mitigation of the traditional and expected six sex penalties: conception, infection, brutalization, ostracism, damnation of deviation and harm to character.

I. First and foremost was pregnancy, labor, child-rearing; the months of disability, the night of intermitting anguish, the years of unremitting watching; the financial stress for the married; for the single, the grave hazards of quack abortion or else a scorn that lasted two lifetimes.

II. Venereal disease contracted from the prostitute bulked large, with the shame, the consequent concealment and the dire sequels of concealment.

III. Brutalization of the male was inevitable and incessant before the days of practical birth control because every sex act forced the man to shut his eyes and harden his heart to the possible consequences for the woman, were she wife, mistress or casual of the night.

IV. Social obloquy for the woman was severe, since, outside of marriage, even momentary yielding to passionate and devoted love branded a woman for life.

V. Perversion has been the label for the substitute sex behaviors resulting mainly from biological thwarting, such as autoeroticism and self-relief (now often regarded as a stage on the way to full function) or the homosexual play that seems mostly sex starvation. Factually, none of these involved many serious consequences in the absence of alarmist teaching or excesses.

VI. Detrimental effect on character appears to have been due in part to insistent doctrines of shamefulness and perversion, to incessant hiding, deceit and intrigue; to the utmost fostering of hypocrisy; to an insistence on the evil in what we now call normal function, fortunately now being replaced by a more worthy, as well as a more intelligent, outlook on this phase of life.

The unmarried adult, like the married, is not unaware that there are ways of avoiding the risks of sexual intercourse, if he or she can only ascertain what is safe. Half-a-million dollars a year is evidently not spent on advertisements in the leading women's magazines describing all kinds of sure "feminine hygiene" and methods of killing "germs" without ample financial rewards. Male protectives are manufactured here at the rate of two million a day, are exceedingly cheap, their quality is improving rapidly and their availability is so general in cities and towns, at drug stores, barber shops and gas stations, that it requires little imagination as to why they are widely employed. The protection afforded is so high and the method so simple that they are accepted as meeting the need of safety wherever the man initiates the precaution or the woman insists upon it.

It is certain that the methods of control of conception are such that no possible law or law enforcement can check their use. A woman can go to a clinic and give a married name and there is no way of knowing what the truth may be for the clinic can scarcely demand the exhibit of a marriage certificate. She may fairly claim the right to know how to protect herself and with equal fairness maintain that the decision when and how to use that protection is her personal concern. The individualized clinic method is approximately ninety-five per cent effective, but is so bothersome that fifty per cent of those instructed return to simpler ways even though these may embody a larger degree of risk. In the future, household remedies or materials will become available that will suffice to meet economic and physical needs. As soon as months-long, years-long protection is discovered, prolonged immunity will ensue and this will call on new mores to deal with further new freedoms. Again we are forced back to our basic stand; we must prepare our defense by education in self-mastery.

Sterilization, without unsexing, has some bearing on the sex side of life of the unmarried and is an important phase of birth control. It rests securely on an extensive surgical experience, having been performed nearly 20,000 times in twenty-seven of our states. This practice has developed as a eugenic measure in institutions for the insane and feeble-minded in order to allow inmates, otherwise unfit, to return to their homes or to work. The increasing recognition of its value is shown by the fact that as many persons were thus treated during the last four years as during the preceding sixteen years. The much-heralded program of Germany is based upon a complete acceptance of its guaranteed benefits. To sterilize either the male or the female, a pair of tiny ducts is closed, and without the danger of any handicap of desire or response. The surgical technique for the man is nearly as simple as that of a dental extraction, and it may become so for the woman. Now its privileges are confined chiefly to those who without it would require segregation for life. Anyone desiring to marry, but unfit to produce children by reason of the likelihood of transmitting some hereditary disease or defect, or those who have had all the children they can bear or rear, will eventually come within the benefits of this relief. Naturally there is apprehension that the measure will be abused by those electing the operation, who may thus gain security for promiscuity, and that it will serve as an open endorsement to aid and abet non-marital mating. This is contrary to experience.

*Abortion,* and not miscarriage, is now the official medical term for any interruption of pregnancy, spontaneous or induced, by anyone at any time before the child, if born, can survive. Public opinion accepts this operation as a frequent necessity, particularly for the unmarried, and therefore does not believe abortion really wrong in most cases. This social attitude is in curious contrast with the uttermost severity of the laws. Although there is at least one known abortion for every four living children born in the city of New York (it is one to one in some parts of Germany), there have been only three convictions of abortionists in the courts in fifteen years. In Philadelphia rigid measures taken against the professional abortionists drove them from the city; there were fewer abortions, but the quality of the work so deteriorated that the death rate from abortion quadrupled. The clever abortionist attains great dexterity from constant practice and can guard himself with the same aseptic precautions that every good surgeon employs. The danger is twofold: first a woman may fall into the hands of an inexpert or unclean operator; and second, the best operative skill will not avail against severe infection in case there has been unclean tampering before the woman comes to the abortionist for operative treatment and care. People fail to comprehend that, notwithstanding the dogmatic advertising claims, no drug actually has the assured power to bring on the delayed period or to interrupt pregnancy. The laity little grasps the danger of waiting, but after three periods are passed skilled experts refuse to operate at all, as is the fact in Russia where there is no stigma in entering a three-hundred-bed abortarium.

In that country, the woman has the doubtful privilege of deciding for herself whether she will undergo the suffering and dangers of labor and the rearing of an unwanted child, or whether she will bear no more children than she can afford to rear.

Happily, a diagnosis of pregnancy now can be made early and with certainty by the method of injecting the woman's urine into an immature rabbit or mouse and noting whether maturity develops in the animal within two to four days—a test available by the time a woman is a week overdue. Thus, wherever necessary, the best time for clearing the uterus (curetting) can be selected, such as the days just before the second period would be due and passed. Hence the unmarried girl pregnant by a married man can be cared for scientifically and thus two people can be saved from lifelong shame or ruin—which is no less true when both parties are unwed. Obviously in these times of bitter poverty, when an additional child is unwelcome because it threatens the economic stability of the family, the multigravid woman offers the doctor his choice of the following: to interrupt; to refer the pregnant woman to a physician skillful and experienced in abortion, but condemned by his own profession; to let this mother of several children run grave risks at the hands of an unclean midwife or ignorant friend; or, most hazardous of all, to allow her to bungle it herself. One-fourth of the deaths connected with pregnancy and labor in New York City followed unskillful abortion by unclean or rough methods. In addition, very many women were infected or invalided or rendered sterile. Most of the rejected non-therapeutic abortions cause sterility. Abortions are not contraceptive; they are destructive of the product of conception. Knowledge of simple and effective birth-control methods, if generally available, would render most abortions unnecessary.

In the female, physical capacity for successful mating is measurable, and sex experience is anatomically self-registering in a degree and with a frequency sufficient to be of wide utility. This is true whether we regard prediction or diagnosis as the crux of our study in the interest of a practical advisory service. To foresee is to forestall difficulties. Most of the multiple troubles described in my *Thousand Marriages* were preventable. Infantile or defective development, the less usual types of genital structure, and, above all, the local conditions calling for special precautions or technique are all so readily detectable that omission of a simple routine examination is not excusable. The physical examination has particular application wherever premarital trial or any form of companionate marriage is contemplated.

The hymen does not admit the normal adult male except after damage by force suddenly applied, or as the result of a course of gradual stretching by phallus, finger or instrumental treatment. The hymen is the measure of vaginal virginity and of this alone, as is testified to by the frequency of psychic sexual response and of mutual bisexual climax without penetration. The hymen fell from its high estate as the gauge of genuine chastity as soon as we fully faced and analyzed sexual fantasy. It lost its preëminence as the guardian against conception the moment free entrance became feasible without hazard of pregnancy. Exalting and conserving the hymen will fall into bad physiological repute as soon as we decide that youthful and premarital self-relief is usual and not of itself abnormal. When that idea is granted, we shall teach that any method of self-relief that focusses and then fixes the site of sensation and response exclusively on the external region, and is restricted to this area, tends to defeat the internal responses which are essential to mutual balance in physical union.

The evidence for the foregoing statements—some of them anatomical heresies—may be found in certain of my books, written, not from theories bred in a library or from animals mated in the laboratory, but from the lips and looks and acts of live, and very human, beings.

The doctor finds no greater change in any attitude than that encountered among educated members of the younger generation concerning the subject once damned by being called self-abuse, solitary vice, pollution, perversion, and the name that carries all these implications, masturbation. With the emerging opinion of the scientist and the unbiased student that the practice is commonly moderate, harmless and natural during certain stages of life—and with the excess relatively infrequent—it is to be hoped that the word masturbation and its connotations will be displaced by a term like autoeroticism or autosexuality, as well as by a saner outlook upon the entire subject.

Among the thousand unmarried college graduates of the Davis series, two-thirds reported autoerotic practice at some time. More than a third of those admitting the experience stopped it within a year; half of them carried it on from ten to thirty years; of those who were continuing at the date of report, one-third nad continued it from twenty to thirty years. One-half of the autoerotic group did not follow through to a climax (although it was usual in the Dickinson series). Correlation between autoeroticism and health among the third that never experimented, the third that discontinued soon and the third that continued for many years showed "a real difference in the way of better health among those keeping on with the practice." No appreciable difference in health was noted between those who began early and those who started after age eighteen. Effects were noted as good or negative, by 61 per cent of those reporting. Hamilton found that 74 of the 100 wives studied by him had had autosexual experience at some time in their lives. The Dickinson-Beam study of histories and physical examinations, mostly of professional women, led him to believe that 63 per cent of the married had had the experience, and his discussions with single women led to a confirmation of the practice among 85 per cent. Considering the signs and discussion of nearly 500 women, married and single, the verbal statements confirmed the anatomical findings in eleven out of twelve cases.

If then, as implied by several series of studies, the frequency of autoeroticism among women amounts to 66 2/3 per cent to 85 per cent, it would seem to be so general an experience as to warrant calling it a natural phenomenon, possibly a provision of nature looking toward a response in later completed sex activity.

Among the male college graduates examined by Peck and Wells, 40 per cent acknowledged, and only 4 per cent denied, autoeroticism. Mierowsky, in his study, established the figure of frequency as 70 per cent. Scremin found the practice very general among male students, with guilt reactions dwindling. Stekel classified masturbation as a physiological process. Bleuler and also Wechsler doubt that masturbation is the cause of psychosis. Freud withdrew from his earlier idea that neurasthenia was due to its prolonged and excessive practice. Students of psychic disorders are said by Malamud to call masturbation an important causative factor because of the perilous psychic attitudes toward its sequelae and not because of the habit itself.

Malamud and Palmer, in their 1932 study of the rôle played by masturbation in the causation of mental disturbance, regarded autoeroticism as a factor in only 10 per cent of 500 patients, mainly among males and at adolescence. Any dire effect was attributed by these authors not to any actual organic injury, but to a psychic conflict—the result of erroneous beliefs concerning the effects of the practice and its ethical and moral implications. In those instances, where the autoeroticism seemed to be the prime factor and in which the fears of the patients could be allayed, the outcome was favorable for 80 per cent of the sufferers. The failures were in the instances where other causes were more fundamental. They reported no cases of actual excess of the practice. These findings are in general accord with the answers to my inquiries, when visiting California hospitals for the insane to study sterilization.

The 1933 findings of Strakosch in her investigation of 700 psychopathic women were very nearly the same as those reported by Davis or Dickinson, but the psychopaths showed a greater tendency to continue the autoerotic practice, owing perhaps to their segregation and inactive life. Strakosch also found that the age at beginning more generally approximated 15 to 17 years. She recorded a greater occurrence of excessive frequencies and a very much higher proportion of the feeling of guilt and shame. Victims of dementia praecox showed no more addiction than balanced people of social normalcy. She concluded that there was little positive evidence that sex *per se* is of importance in the differential development of the psychotic or psychoneurotic personality.

A favorite alarmist threat against autoeroticism is that it will seriously interfere with happiness in marriage. I do not know of data concerning males, but there is important evidence concerning women. A Davis series testifies that the practice did not unfavorably influence sex relations; that in the earlier years of marriage pleasurable reactions were significantly higher, although responsiveness persisted longer in the group that never had been autoerotic. In my cases, persistence in self-relief, or resort to it after marriage, occurred among wives whose husbands had an inadequate technique or were premature in their completions.

Homosexuality has been stressed far beyond its numerical significance or its importance as a harmful interference with normal response. Physiology is teaching us that we are all in some degree bisexual and that we possess some sex traits other than those characteristic of our overt type, with two series of stages between extreme masculinity and complete femininity. No better example could be brought forward of the unfortunate course of human sex study than that in its beginning it took up the bizarre, the abnormal and the extreme, rather than average normal sex conduct. We were shocked with dramatized horrors. Suppose one or two per cent of men and women have blood chemistry that turns them toward their own sex and disqualifies them for marriage. The actual evil therefrom is limited to the small number who solicit young people and who must be prevented from holding teaching or guiding positions. As I know the trend among women, it is a sex starvation or a demonstration of affection rather simple and occasional. Half of the college women reporting to Dr. Davis had had a homosexual emotional experience and half of these acknowledged its physical expression. To stamp such activity a "perversion," instead of a deviation or deprivation, is to lack a sense of proportion, if not sound judgment. These people generally turn to the other sex whenever the opportunity presents.

One might consider gauging the rate of change in sexual belief and practice among the unmarried by the ratios found in three groups of patients to whom I had offered free counsel concerning marriage. The non-virgins in a half-hundred women of 1895 constituted approximately 20 per cent; in a similar group of 1929–1930, 33 1/3 per cent; in those studied in 1933–1934, 50 per cent. To these near-marriages must be added the numbers who had found the relief of the "all-but-virgin" mounting in the third series to 25 per cent. These sample groups include graduates of nineteen colleges. It is to be noted particularly that the full marital privilege was adopted, on the average, only after a twelve-month of increasing demonstration of affection. Moreover, periods of economic hardship distinctly lengthen engagements of the modern professional groups well beyond the former two-year period, while multiplying the intimacies—faithfulness holding fast meanwhile.

If this is a fair indication of premarital experience, one might conclude that, having been refused companionate marriage, youth has turned to companionate engagement. As we show in *The Single Woman,* in four successive decades there has been a difference according to social status. Girls and women in personal service tend to have a relation brief and physical, with an undue proportion of pregnancy and venereal disease. Among clerical workers there is a considerable frequency of an unfortunate outcome, but a longer period of constant devotion than in the first group and less demand for medical treatment or abortion. With the professional women and students, it is almost altogether a case of the one-and-only-man: "Our group are all full-fledged monogamists—at least as long as love lasts"—with venereal infection absent and conception rare.

One is impressed with the steadiness and considerateness of the engaged male under trying circumstances, his full acceptance by the girl's family, the gradual arrival at a conviction of the rightness and inevitableness of the relations with "my wife" and "my husband," and profound regret for the need of deception and intrigue. "Of course we want to get married and have babies; our two families were going to help us, but now they can't any more, and they won't let us marry till he can support me. I've landed a job, and I'll get more than he does—and that's not very pleasant for him."

What effect on health has complete abstention from intercourse or the suppression of every outlet for desire? Obviously there are different effects among the single and the married. A normal wedded couple living under the intimacies which inevitably arouse feeling, yet undertaking repression, suffer from stresses very much greater than do the single who avoid stimulating situations. We ask whether there are penalties to be paid for non-use of the sex function. Yes and no. The organs do not shrink from neglect as muscles do. Any harm is mainly to the nervous system. In my records of married and unmarried, the type suffering from nervous unbalance is a virgin, a young woman of superior family and without occupation, worrying and feeling herself in the wrong. The strain upon emotional balance probably is primarily in proportion to the functional vigor of the particular pair of glands, male or female, and its resistance to suppression. Under favorable circumstances, adult sex organs function on the average slightly more frequently than twice a week, but the range of intensity, measured as frequency, is wide, running from once a month to daily or more often—all being compatible with good health and active work. The new knowledge of our internal chemistry and of the hormones or "excitants" makes it quite clear why there may be enormous differences in sex endowment, capacity and drive in different people. This reveals a status that is based upon physical factors instead of representing, as we had supposed, a matter of morals in resisting or in yielding to temptation. Here again a new orientation is in order.

Only an ample series of case histories and physical examinations will enable us to determine what part of a sex urge or excessive stress is the result of regular or seasonal cycles of hormone production, and what part is activated by mental preoccupations with stimulative ideas or by exposure to influences calculated to render alert and active the function of the sex organs. The moralist insists that continence in the unmarried is wholly compatible with good health, unimpaired capacity for wonted work and reasonable serenity, and that there is no need for ever prescribing intercourse outside of marriage; it may be true, but the scientist is still asking for actual evidence and proof in place of mere opinion and he has not yet received it. There is considerable evidence that the male cannot arrest the activity of his glands or actually sublimate their function. Records appear to demonstrate that the female child is aware of local sensations earlier than the male, but that the adult woman possesses less sexual urge and capacity than the man, at least under her present conditions. The only conclusions at which one can arrive at present is that every problem of personal sexual maladjustment must be decided on its own merits and only after due study.

What changes in policy and policing indicate a possibility of more direct discussion and action? Stated baldly, the alternatives have been, and still are, either an all-inclusive distrust, backed by a perfected spy system covering individual and community, or second, trustworthiness and moderation begotten by training for character, self-control, and consideration for others. The first of these philosophies was consistently acted upon by the Mohammedan when he locked up his womenkind; by the Spaniard with his ever vigilant duenna; by the peasant in the home where the young girl was never left alone with any male not of the family; by the French who married off a daughter directly from the convent; by mid-Victorian chaperonage with no time free of watch and ward; by the Briton whose law permits him to beat his wife for talk with other men; by the American who insists that he is to be the only male comrade or mental stimulus. All of these have for a motive an unsleeping suspicion.

The pendulum is sweeping full swing. The girl is on her way to become socially independent, the unmarried woman to be financially and legally independent. Either may come and go with little requirement of report on the use of her free time, even for the hour after the party broke up and before she reached home. There is social acceptance or, at least, tolerance of behavior capable of the most active sexual stimulation, like the multiple cocktail, "I pass out at the second"; dancing in thinnest bodycover with bared back, in rhythms of closest front-pressures and with interlacing thighs; general petting or necking with its variants and its variety of limits, wherein the deep kiss is the standard initial test to determine whether either one allows further or furthest arousing. There is the literature of passion everywhere available; the bareness at beach and in sports; the twosome on hike and vacation; the automobile parked in the dark or the by-road; the ubiquitous tourist welcome (though with a book to sign); the week-end with youngsters alone on top floors. There is a great increase in the number of small apartments for young men or women without restriction as to callers or their hours of visiting; and acquiescence in visitors in the single room that is a bedroom—above all, there is the job away from Hometown in the Big City, "where no one will know."

Will anything but self-mastery offset such conditions? Or will exhaustion of the capacity for excitation numb all this stimulus, in the same way that the removal of sexual suggestiveness from nakedness can come, and only come, by completeness of nakedness? The artist and the doctor bear witness to this possibility.

Where is the middle course between liberty and license? When do we begin to survey this ground, and on its new highway set up directional arrows and danger signs? Our conditions are as different as our speeds are different from the days of the horse-drawn vehicle and the dress that must cover the ankles to protect against an accusation of intentional sensuality. One survey has already begun. A vast nation is experimenting with freedom of intercourse, easy marriage and simple divorce. Is, or is not, Russia showing that human nature is far more reasonable, moderate and trustworthy than we ever dared hope? Two half-hours a week and no mystery puts sex in its place as an incident, intense as is no other. A philosophy and a régime that has wrecked so many lives and marriages cannot be deemed a success. At last, in the search for the good life, an effort is being made to seek for the good in sex life with all possible avoidance of failure. And Russia merits careful watching.

Looked at as physiology and divorced from morals, there is a curious contrast between the somewhat common pattern of a progressive youthful solution of sex life and the traditional standard behavior. Many of my records of premarital sex practice run true to a type. Beginning with interest or friendship and mounting wonder, going on to glamor and romance, the expressions of affection gradually take more definite form, as a whole year runs its course. The deep kiss leads on to caresses that by degrees grow more and more intimate up to the point of mutual climax, then to near-marital privilege, then to full privilege and nights together. There is an early time of doubt and guilt, followed by a full justification built on completeness of trust in each other and perfected adjustments. "Her soul he knows not from her body, neither from God." Undiscovered, they put away apprehension and grieve at the need of furtive love-making.

Compare this with the standard procedure, blessed of heaven. During two years of engagement no affectionate touch must start an impure thought nor arouse the imagination to picture what is to happen at the consummation of marriage. On the night following the promissory ceremony, in some strange room or in a narrow berth of train or ship, two tired people, strangers to each other's bodies, are thrust together, made more or less aware of their nakedness, in order that he may boldly make sure that she is a virgin.

Which is wicked? Which is natural? Which is making for enduring romance and adventure? Which looks toward frigidity and disgust and divorce? One of them is barbarous, as biology, and criminal, as sociology. Where lies good sense—still in terms of physiology divorced from morals?

With the new orientation of all sex activities now under way, religion is confronted with a situation not unlike that which occurred when a radical series of discoveries brought action from the supporters of dogmatic theology that alienated nearly all scientists and drove them from the church.

As with adventures in science, so the church may now estrange inquiring youth. It can do this by a continued defamation of sex feelings and expressions instead of by re-studying the whole subject. Youth is ahungered for things of the spirit. The process of recasting moral values has begun with the acceptance of sex union as a cement of love in marriage, and not merely as an act solely for procreation. I have mentioned that many urgent and variant sex capacities formerly supposed to be moral, as well as traits and tendencies still regarded as immoral, are consequences of internal chemistry or of anatomical structure. If this radical modification of facts is affecting our teaching and thinking, is it not reasonable to believe that there are other points of view that may be subject to revaluations? The discredit that came to the church as the result of its attitudes toward astronomy and geology and toward the history of man upon the earth should not be repeated in this matter of sex. One such challenge to religious influence has already happened in a recent pronouncement concerning control of conception. It should be a warning to all who believe in spiritual values. It should awaken all who hope for a spiritual revival to do their part toward promoting sex sanity.

A single family can present a rather extreme range of clinical evidence. More than thirty years ago I delivered three babies in a sincerely religious family of fine heredity. The older sister married a fine fellow after a two-year engagement during which their affection was carefully limited to a brother-and-sister kiss. All their information centered about an understanding that on the wedding night something had to be "got over." And he performed his marital duty so effectively that a tired girl was shell-shocked and retained her dread and spasms, even after a miscarriage and two deliveries. Her brother had a still longer engagement to a girl, like himself, possessed with the strong religious emotion that is normally paralleled by deep sexual emotion. They saw each other almost every evening. As physical excitement developed strongly, they checked its further expression and even the admission of it to each other. By the time they were married they had built so high a wall of inhibition at a given point of erotic arousing that they never have been able to surmount its arresting effect upon each other although both are in danger in the presence of others with whom they are conscious that completion would be possible.

The third child, aware of the tensions and maladjustments of these two admired couples, at the age of seventeen declared that she would never marry. There was a friendly bachelor, who was like an uncle to all these people and was their ultimate confidant in all personal affairs, but he had been abroad for a long time. On his return he took the brilliant and popular second sister in training and in a year gradually taught her the full technique of sex expression. She also had a long engagement but with marital ways after the first year; and after marriage she had two children. Later, in her widowhood, as two second cousins came to their active sexual urges, she began to educate the lads along the same lines for which she was deeply grateful to the "uncle." The unhappy and dissatisfied pairs and the wholesome and whole-souled widow were my patients but I may not live long enough to learn what happened to the young men trained by this serene, cultured woman. Possibly her influence may have fixed the level of sexual compatibility in happiness for their future wives, as occurred in another such instance.

In my visit to fourteen countries in 1926, I heard everywhere the statement that the prostitute was complaining that her business was steadily dwindling. A high authority like Peller declares this vocation to be doomed. The wife, with protection against excessive childbearing in her own control, need no longer refuse the husband; he need not stray from home. Nor is the youth who cannot marry, who formerly feared to impregnate a beloved, nearly so prone to resort to the prostitute. Old unmarried men appear to be their remaining clients. The lessening of syphilis, reported by Pinkus, seems to be one eugenic result of the decline of prostitution. Russia has set the world an example by placing prostitutes in re-training institutions under government control, by reclaiming them physically and socially; and by making prostitution unnatural and unnecessary in the social order because marriage and divorce have been simplified.

My records afford very little evidence correlating sexual maladjustment exclusively with disorders and diseases of the female pelvic organs. Occasionally mild inflammations may follow frequently repeated auto-erotism, or there may be the torment of excitation without an orgasm. The health of the unmarried and the health of the married, in terms of the pelvic organs, show no great difference save for the effects of labor. Sexual adjustment inheres in psychic adaptation far more than in genital or reproductive structure.

The capacity and the desire for work, love, or for sexual practice in any form continue far beyond the middle years when subsidence is popularly taken for granted. The women I have studied always looked first for love in their heterosexual experience and apparently they turned to relations bringing about a mere physical satisfaction only after a disappointment in love. Marriage remained the greatest desire of all of them.

My notes on unmarried women during the past five decades indicate a continuing movement toward the separation of sex and love, toward the indulgence in physical enjoyments divorced from complete emotional relief, with all the dangers that are implied for monogamy and all the hazards that are said to threaten personality. The educated unmarried group possess general knowledge of the feasibility of birth control, together with a reasonable curiosity about methods and their trustworthiness; there is, also, after eating from the tree of knowledge, honest blessing on "what makes this Glory possible." Indeed, while the simple male protective is generally known, the grave hazards of unskilled abortion are never sensed, and abortion unfortunately is still considered a ready resource "if anything goes wrong."

"Sexual illiteracy is costly," as Lura Beam insists, and "education usually has a better time than ignorance."

Education in the realm of sex involves a search to discover the relation of sexuality to life and to character as well as to offspring. She notes that the available records show how ambivalent sexuality is. Woman never loves herself without hating herself; if she is hot she will also be cold; if she is not for sexuality she will be against it and for something else. The unmarried woman never performs a sexual act and lives as though it had never happened; this act echoes later in another guise as it has become part of herself.

When marriage fails, the wife may fall into a state of frigidity, experience distress in intercourse and suffer a maladjustment that continues perhaps until divorce; "that is, she stops creating in the rôle of marriage and begins to project herself alone." This projection of self is what the single do in their work, the arts, religion, their relations to the family and to other people. Maladjustment within the self is reflected in disturbances in these and other non-egocentric activities. "Without relation to marital status, the trend is toward individualism."

"The social meaning of singleness, outside of fertility, is in the change of mental and spiritual values implied in development without sexual knowledge and emotional fertilization. . . ." "Singleness is differently ignorant, and differently wise from marriage."

My medical viewpoint may, for convenience in discussion, be stated in generalized terms not now susceptible of more than partial proof.

Non-marriage and non-mating are social and biological thwarting. They constitute the frustration of love-comradeship, child-rearing and home-making. The two functions of sex union being wholesome pleasure and reproduction, the ratio between the urge and the need may be found to be as a hundred to one. All men and women have an endowment and capacity for physical sex expression, but in one-tenth of them, it is defective or inefficient; in another tenth it is high-powered and insistent. For the great group forming eight-tenths of the adults, there is a normal urge for expression two or three times weekly. In this group the swing toward relative frigidity or partial impotence on the one hand, or toward a developed urgency and fullest satisfaction on the other hand, depends upon opportunity or training, or both. The controls are social, and not biological, and medical practice must recognize this fact.

The mitigation or removal of the penalties, physical and social, for the natural sex act are in sight. This represents the beginning of a new attitude toward all varieties of erotic play and sex experimentation, within and outside of marriage. We are in the midst of a new orientation. The traditional degradation of the sex function is doomed; the old mystification will cease; our present hypocrisy will become intolerable. The right of woman to make her own decisions is on the way. We may even hope for her increasingly intelligent leadership in these affairs of the body and soul in which hers is the greatest stake and into which she can put heart and spirit. A hopeful outlook suggests that the best of the old ideas concerning one-man-one-woman life partnership will be strengthened but with a new degree of equality, flexibility and tolerance. A broader knowledge, a deeper understanding and a richer content of marital life can be expected to increase human happiness and multiply the number of successful unions.

# LAW

> Did not human laws restrain the natural liberty of men, every particular marriage would be as different, as contracts or bargains of any other kind of species.
>
> —ALEXANDER HUME

## CHANGING LAWS AND CHANGING ATTITUDES

*Morris L. Ernst*

COUNSELLOR IN VARIOUS LEGAL ACTIONS INVOLVING FEDERAL LAWS RELATING TO LITERARY CENSORSHIP

IN CLEAREST diction our most liberal jurists have declared that we live in a world of change. We read that law accepts as the pattern of its justice the morality of the community whose conduct it assumes to regulate. Hence we should imagine that the principles and practices of the law would follow those men and women of the community whom the social mind ranks as intelligent.

Unfortunately, that is not the case. Seldom does the law correspond to the actual feelings, habits and demands of the community. Too often does the jurist fail to appraise the mores of the day or, even if he makes the attempt, he succumbs to the human failing of deserting objectivity for the warmer and more friendly interpretation of his own personal likes and dislikes as if they were the accepted mood of all the people. Long after the Brandeisian resistances to chain stores and large scale business have been smothered between forgotten buckram, we will recall Louis D. Brandeis for those subtle and stubborn footnotes accompanying many of his opinions in his attempts to find bodies of facts which ineluctably lead to legal conclusions.

But if the courts are not in tune in the realm of mortgages (save where moratoria are induced by the smell of burning bridges and the blockading of milk trucks), or if they remain a decade or more behind the people in matters such as bills of lading or riparian rights, they are surely thirty or fifty years behind the lives of our people on all subjects that derive from sexual motivations.

This lengthening gap is only natural. Just as individuals find it more difficult to adjust to emotional than to intellectual situations, so do the legislatures and the courts evidence their greatest ineptitude whenever they try to govern the emotional lives of men and women.

Three centuries ago emotional adventurists ran foul of the law by subscribing to the theory that the earth was round. Devotion to the Copernican doctrine led to the gallows. The old ecclesiastical courts surely retarded progress by condemning to limbo those intellectual concepts which aroused the sternest emotions. In Tennessee within a decade the Darwinian theory boiled up fundamentalist emotions and again the courts remained stubborn.

As a moderator of commercial customs the judicial system has been successful. Justice then seems wide-eyed. Non-mathematical emotional material has a blinding influence on men in robes. Cases involving sexual expression transmute our judges into a group of legalistic Rip Van Winkles—shielding their eyes from the light. In such matters Justice is truly blind.

Let us examine the gap between the law and the sexual habits of adults in the United States. The facts as I see them indicate a scene which obviously is a mixture derived from situations that reveal an amalgam of the philosophies of the Greeks and the Jews. Greece, a small land and overcrowded, condoned Lesbianism, encouraged homo-sexuality, and did not frown on infanticide. Adultery and fornication were invited by that people living in a land of food scarcity.

The Jews were a small people ruled by a God who ordered them to multiply. Celibacy was a disgrace, masturbation and all forms of homosexuality were considered anti-social, and for many centuries before the Prophets polygamy was the order of the day. The Jews needed a larger population and hence adultery and fornication were taboo as being without hope for progeny. Remarriage was approved and in certain circumstances virtually ordered.

In this land of ours we find mirrored this Greco-Jewish amalgam. Remarriage is not considered adulterous. Five hundred thousand men and women pour through our divorce courts each year and the total of spouses separated or divorced runs into more than eight millions in the country. Fornication for men is an accepted practice and for women it is looked upon today as a variation and no longer as a disgrace. The gap between the age of urge for sexual intercourse and the time when our economic system permits the financial support of a spouse is too long successfully to banish fornication. Adultery as one expression of this failure is coming out into the open more and more. In the last ten years the courts of New York State alone gave some evidence of adultery by 50,000 men and women. This must be but a negligible proportion of the total adulterous acts committed in the Empire State during that decade, and it does not indicate the share attributable to unmarried paramours.

Polygamy, as such, does not exist, but another search of the court records of claims against married men for support, and of bequests left to friendly females by deceased bankers, forces one to believe that many men are supporting financially more than a wife, and that they no doubt are receiving at least sexual comfort outside of the legal residence.

In Sparta men put their wives nude in public places for the admiring gaze of the populace. Thus was their own wisdom of selection vindicated. In all of our large cities nearly nude chorus girls draw large crowds of visiting merchants who come in from smaller cities to learn about life and to do some business. These nude dancers are popular with the masses of the people. Many of them are the testimonialists whose signatures are invoked to induce larger sales of soaps, creams or popular breast covers. Their opinions are heralded as those of leaders in the community.

I have found no accurate evidence of the extent of homosexuality in the records of the judicial system, but the growing practice of segregation of homosexuals in prisons and hospitals at least gives evidence of the recognition of those ways of living as being accepted by more than incidental portions of the public.

Several years ago our leading literary censors endeavored to suppress Mary Ware Dennett's pamphlet, in part because of the references therein to masturbation. The New York Society for the Suppression of Vice, through its counsel, was fearful that our civilization would totter if people knew that nearly all men and women have masturbated but did not know that the most valid objection to such act lay in the destructive consciousness of guilt that arises in the minds of most people. The courts allowed the pamphlet free circulation and thus by indirection at least acknowledged the probability of truth in Mrs. Dennett's statements about masturbation.

I have not endeavored to appraise the extent of statutory or non-statutory rape, the prevalence of prenuptial agreements, the number of marital annulments acted on by our courts. These are side streams to the main channels of sex expression which I have mentioned.

Assuming that all of the main sexual urges are instincts rather than social habits, nevertheless the customs and laws of the Greeks and the Jews twisted these instincts into what were to those peoples desirable conventions. So in our civilization the state of the laws and the court decisions may be viewed as possible controllers of sexual life, although the sanctity of Law has faded and nullification by the people or by judicial wheedling has become an uncomfortable but valuable saving grace. Let us now consider to what extent the courts are in rapport with the social customs of our people. Possibly the conflict between our mores and our laws must be charged against the weird endeavor of treating a Greco-Jewish amalgam with doses of Roman-Anglo-Saxon Law. I should imagine that those areas of the United States which inherited a Napoleonic Law Code found a more flexible jurisprudence than the greater part of the country laboring under the light-minded legalisms of Blackstone.

The foremost mandate of the judicial branch of the government in matters gonadic has been to insist on ignorance. Sexual knowledge had to be kept from the young. Writings on toilet walls, crayon markings on stoops and sidewalks, were the main source of sexual education. Adults might swap filthy stories in Pullman smokers or sneakily pass around disgusting scatological post cards imported from abroad. But no children should ever learn that sex was as natural as inquiring about it, that venereal disease was curable or that the sexual act was the greatest known physical joy of human beings. Until a very few years ago the Government of the United States through the Post Office Department and the Federal Attorney General's office endeavored to keep such ideas away from young boys and girls.

Adults had to be content with the stilted evasions and the dishonest sexual enlightenment allowed to children —which, of course, was worse than nothing at all. The law associated a lack of sexual knowledge with some mysterious form of legalized righteousness. Our government was fearful that if married adults were allowed to purchase enlightened sexual literature those same words could not be kept from the unmarried. Hence the entire population was put on a diet of bootlegged sexual information and the married were too frequently later victims of their mandated ignorance as unmarried adults.

Few people realize that from the founding of this nation until 1870 there were practically no legal restrictions on the sale or distribution of literature or contraceptives. George Washington, so fearful of Postal Censorship, conceived of a post office as a mechanical conduit and recommended that mail be carried without charge so as to avoid the invitation of censorship. Even when the Southern States were in jeopardy because of incendiary abolitionist literature, the Senate of the

United States, with Clay, Calhoun and Webster sitting, voted that any censorship of the mails would be unlawful.

Not until 1870 did we renounce the faith of the Founding Fathers, when Anthony Comstock shipped to Washington a carload of postal cards and pictures for display to our then representatives. And they became so agitated and fearful for their fellow citizens that they dignified obscenity by enacting the absurd law against obscenity, still part of our criminal statutes.

From 1870 to 1915 the courts suppressed quantities of books by accepting the ideas and interpretation applied to obscenity by Comstock, Sumner and Chase—our three leading professional stalkers of lewdness.

During the past fifteen years a marked change has taken place. The laws written by Congress and the many legislatures have not been amended. The words Obscene, Lustful, Lascivious and Indecent have not been erased. They are all spelled with the same old letters and in the same old ways. But the courts, makers of the law, have been forced to recognize the vast amount of nullification which has taken place—not nullification of the acts of legislatures but open, defiant nullification of the prior decisions of courts defining these obscenity laws. The old words had to be re-defined so that the courts would not be laughed out of court. Then what happened?

Novels making light of fornication and derisive of sexual fidelity were allowed free and open circulation. *Mlle. de Maupin* contained a foreword by the author decrying sexual virtue. *The Well of Loneliness,* condemned in the lower court, was removed from the ban on appeal on the stated ground that a theme—in that case Lesbianism—was not to be censored under the head-ing of Obscenity. *God's Little Acre,* containing picturesque scenes of genital kissing, received more than legal approval from a wise magistrate. *Jurgen* was freed because of sophistication and Feuchtwanger's *Power* because of its length. *Ulysses,* by James Joyce, was declared by the Treasury Department of the United States to be a classic and as such admissible into the United States from abroad despite the use of certain Anglo-Saxon words.

The courts that had been so blind and remiss for four decades compensated by vacillating and squirming, by advancing, by legal backsliding. Any excuse was good enough. Books which the libraries, newsstands, literary critics and editorial writers had accepted and openly dealt in had to be declared immune from the legal ban. Only once or twice have the courts been courageous enough to say: "We were wrong; we erred. Ignorance cannot be the law of the land. We reverse our bigotries. We don't care about the author's fame or his intent, nor the size or the makeup of the book. If it is accepted it must be legal, and by acceptance we do not intend to be guided by the morons, the infants or those fearing folk who think that sex itself is a dirty thing." Some day a court will write that and then go one step further and acquaint the legal brethren with the simple fact that sexual stimuli abound in life and that the printed word is probably one of the least of sexual provocatives. Courts may some day refuse to pass upon non-aphrodisiac works of fiction.

The courts cast their blackest shadows by enforcing the birth control statutes passed by Congress and the various states about 1870. The past sixty years of taboo on contraceptives followed our first hundred years of complete freedom to publish advice on the prevention of conception. If you are in doubt about the real, old-fashioned American mores, look over the files of the *New York Tribune* or the *New York Herald* during the pre-Comstock era. There the married or unmarried, the old and the young, could read columns on columns of advertisements commending and urging various contraceptive tablets and jellies, most of which were probably none too effective. But legal they were, without a doubt.

From 1870 on, the adults of this nation whispered to each other various protective prescriptions. Condoms and other devices were sold to married and unmarried men in stealthy fashion from under the counters of drug stores. That adult laymen grew up uninformed and ignorant was bad enough, but the real vice in this situation was the degradation of the medical profession. The ingenuity of the American medical mind was locked up and scarcely made an effort to escape. Doctors came to believe and act as though even experimental research for an esthetic and fool-proof birth control device were an unclean pursuit. And the American Medical Association has not had either the courage or the honesty to accept a resolution to investigate the medical aspects of the subject or the relative efficiency and hazards of various contraceptives now available and employed. Through pharmacists, the profession came to be silent partners with illicit dealers in rubber devices imported from abroad. The distribution of birth control devices was camouflaged in dishonest excuses, feigned diagnoses of ailments or protection against, or for, the treatment of imagined female diseases.

Around 1915 Margaret Sanger and Mary Ware Dennett started to dramatize the dangers of a sexually ignorant adult population. Slowly the courts started in their usual way to whittle away the laws as written by assemblymen and congressmen. The highest court of New York State sustained a conviction for dispensing birth control information but went out of its way to point out that such information could be legally spread if it were for the purpose of preventing disease. If the court had stopped short at that point nothing much would have been gained by Margaret Sanger's first battle. But the court picked up its little Webster's Standard Dictionary and found that the word "disease" was well defined in the volume. A broad, generous definition it was. Any threatened ailment was within the definition.

About a decade later the courts had another opportunity to define the scope of their own definition. The first Birth Control Clinic was raided in New York City. Records of patients were taken by the police. The medical records of patients were lost or stolen; at least, they were not returned to the physicians. This breach of confidential sanctity shocked the medical high priests into action. They poured into the magistrate's court to testify that improper spacing of children was a threat to good health. The magistrate held that ill health or the threat to good health came within the four corners of the Webster definition of disease. The criminal charges were dismissed.

Having lived through several of the recent trials involving birth control laws, I am quite confident that the courts would now find that the word "disease" covers also the constitutional state of a wife married to an unemployed workman. In time the definition will be stretched to include neurotic strains, fears and even whims. There can be no limit to what the courts will have to do because they dare not allow the present open nullification of the birth control laws to continue.

As long as ill-advised prosecutors or vice agents insist on bringing cases to courts, the judges must do their duty—the simple task of fitting the decisions to the desires of the people. For the sake of my friends on the bench I wish that no more cases were to be brought. It would be more comfortable to have the birth control laws simply die as did so much of the moral control legislation of the late 17th and early 18th centuries. The Federal laws will be amended to meet the facts of life, as our small familial legislators appear to have learned them, when they recognize that their re-election will not be threatened by discarding their stupid hypocrisy.

In 1634 the Massachusetts authorities were alarmed by the introduction of certain new and immodest fashions and prohibited certain types of garments including "slashed clothes, other than one slash in each sleeve and another in the back." Another law also proscribed "short sleeves whereby the nakedness of the arm may be discovered in the wearing thereof." In other colonies, to prevent the widespread practice of what would now be called petting, laws were passed forbidding young men "to inveigle or draw the affections of any maid," without the proper permission, and the current prohibited methods were enumerated "whether it be by speech, writing, message, company-keeping, unnecessary familiarity, disorderly night-meetings, sinful dalliance, or gifts." In one instance a case came up under the statute and the frank young miss denied that her affections had been inveigled. The court thereupon fined her instead of him and called her a "bould virgin." No young man under twenty-one or young woman under eighteen was permitted to be out after nine o'clock at night without parental permission and young people were forbidden to meet in company on Saturday or Sunday evening unless for religious purposes. In one instance, in Connecticut, a young man and woman were prosecuted vigorously for "sitting together on the Lord's Day under an apple tree in Goodman Chapman's orchard." Various laws were passed interdicting dancing; the legislative bodies in several instances commenting that they were sensible of its profaneness, especially of the younger set "taking their opportunity of meeting in places of public entertainment to corrupt one another by their uncivil and wanton carriage." And as a last illustration of these earlier methods, I refer to Alexander Hamilton, one of the sexually gayest of the Founders of the nation, who never tired in his campaign against Maypole parties.

All of these laws have been repealed by legislatures or courts and still the adults in this country are far from a civilized free-and-open market in contraceptives. A recent Federal Court did make some progress toward nullification. A manufacturer of condoms found a competitor stealing his trade-mark. He sued to prevent the unfair competition. In this case of Young Rubber Corporation, Inc., *versus* C. I. Lee & Company, Inc., the courts tried to avoid passing on this lecherous article. A little persistence on the part of counsel brought forth one of the most amusing decisions of this era. The court held that it was legal to send such condoms through the mails or in other fashion if sent to druggists, physicians, and public health officers. Incidentally, this particular brand was being dispensed to the extent of twenty millions a year, as the evidence showed. The Court found that the law forbade only articles intended solely for birth control and that this particular article might be intended for the prevention of disease. In fact,

Congress must have meant to ban only those articles which are exclusively usable for the prevention of conception. Otherwise, every douche bag or syringe would be illegal. By analogy, pessaries, and, in fact, all methods of contraception, likewise became legal because we always get back to that broad and friendly definition of disease written by Mr. Webster.

A few sentences from the Circuit Court of Appeals decision will be illuminating:

> Taken literally, this language (the birth control legislation of the Federal Government) would seem to forbid the transportation by mail or common carriage of anything "adapted," in the sense of being suitable or fitted, for preventing conception or for any indecent or immoral purpose, even though the article might also be capable of legitimate uses and the sender in good faith supposed that it would be used only legitimately. Such a construction would prevent mailing to or by a physician of any drug or mechanical device "adapted" for contraceptive or abortifacient uses, although the physician desired to use or to prescribe it for proper medical purposes. The intention to prevent a proper medical use of drugs or other articles merely because they are capable of illegal uses is not lightly to be ascribed to Congress. (45 F. 2nd, 103.)

All of the above is historically interesting, and indicative of the disingenuous approach of jurisprudence to emotional matters and, in the final analysis, none too beneficial to the adults of this land. Contraceptive devices are shockingly high in price, none too good in quality, by no means readily accessible to all who need them, and often emotionally disturbing. The medical profession remains uninspired, paying far more attention to a pain in the ear than to birth and its voluntary control. Even in 1934, the profession refused to investigate the subject, despite the significant revelations of a shockingly high maternal mortality rate.

During the sixty years since 1870, while pedagogy was making striking advances and social hygiene became a glamorous force, the statutes and the courts have been niggardly in allowing the adult population to gain even a shadowy benefit from their development. Slowly, and often by indirection, judges of the higher courts have partially nullified the thwarting acts of our legislators. This is the outstanding contribution of laws to the sexual behaviors of our adult population.

Aside from birth control and censorship of reading, the basic sexual laws of this country are much the same as in the Colonial Puritan days. Control over adultery and fornication are still deemed possible by inserting clauses in the penal statutes.

Only two marked changes exist. In the first place, we have either repealed or, what is more usual, actually disregarded those quaint old statutes which forbade a man kissing even his wife on the Sabbath or a maiden wearing her hair in braids on the street. In the second place we have altered the punishment for what were considered unsocial forms of sexual expression.

In many New England States adultery laws were taken over bodily from the Colonial decrees. Instead of pillory or stocks, jail sentences or fines were imposed. In some instances the amounts of the fines or the length of the prison sentences have not been changed for a hundred years. It might be argued, with the decreased purchasing power of money, that a two-hundred-dollar fine for fornicating in 1834 was a much more severe penalty than a like fine in 1934; however, any growth in leniency should not be credited to conscious generosity on the part of legislators but rather to monetary fluctuations. Geoffrey May has written very entertainingly on this phase of penalty for sex expression and in fact points to the town of Cardiff, partly in Maryland and partly in Pennsylvania, in which ambiterritorial vicinage adultery on one side of a street is met with a ten-dollar fine, whilst across the lane the same act can lead to a payment of five hundred dollars or a year in jail.

But these variations in punishment are of little significance. Surely greenbacks payable to the State (before or after the shift from a gold standard) never kept man or woman from sexual experience. Although fornication is unlawful in practically every state of the union, arrest, indictment, trial or conviction for such a crime is nearly impossible. The adultery statutes are likewise virtually dead letters. Worthington and Topping have analyzed some of the court returns in larger centers showing, in cases brought for fornication, adultery or lewd and lascivious cohabitation, final commitments of a trifle over one per cent of those so charged. As a blackmail device the laws against fornication are still of some use.

An interesting sidelight on the legal point of view toward the crime of adultery can be seen in the recent history of New York State. Until the regime of Charles Evans Hughes as Governor, adultery was lawful for man or woman. Adultery had been the sole ground for divorce in New York State. A league with some such name as National Christian League for the Advancement of Adult Purity urged the present adultery statute of the Empire State, with two hundred and fifty dollars fine, six months in jail, or both. Thousands of divorces had gone through the New York divorce mill, and continue to do so. It was hoped that by making adultery a crime it would throttle divorce or convict two people in each divorce case. We soon found that prosecutions for adultery under this criminal statute were not pressed by the prosecutors save in cases where the complainant had high influence or some other true complaint existed against the same person but evidence was lacking for the conviction for the real grievance.

I am quite convinced that legal prohibitions placed on fornication and adultery are by no means deterrents for married or unmarried males or females. To be sure, in some of the smaller communities these sex laws are invoked with greater ease and somewhat more success. But even where the desire of the official is most official, the courts have had to go very far in order to jail an alleged malefactor. One of our most philosophical jurists has stretched the law by the following dictum: Proof of an adulterous inclination in the minds of the parties and of an opportunity to satisfy it justifies an inference of sexual intercourse. To this another court has in effect replied: Hugging and kissing for a half hour without interruption in a cemetery is not sufficient for a conviction either of adultery or fornication. And only recently with the rise of the feminist movement man's insecurity has increased and the olden offence of marado has been reinvoked. This is a sort of aggravated adultery because the offence of intercourse takes place in the husband's home.

There is, however, one field of law which has and still does influence to a real degree the unmarried adult. I refer to the law of contracts. Breach of promise of marriage cases certainly shorten the correspondential egos of most males. These actions for the most part are low, legalized blackmail proceedings. It is high time that we do away with the entire right to such an action or at least provide that no action for money damages will lie unless a date for a wedding has actually been set and engraved notices have been sent out. For my part, I would specify in the statute the type of engraving so as to stamp the potential blackmailer right at the print shop.

Alienation of affection cases are of the same breed and have even less integrity. Neither of these legal causes are for the common people. They are only applicable in real life for the rich or, at least, against the rich. Alienation of affection is in itself an impossibility. And the evidence usually proves that the only treasure alienated is a diamond ring or a streamline automobile. I have often wanted to try one of these cases in terms of modern psychology. What kind of lover was this man whom two women want and struggle for? Was his affection ever worth anything? How can it be gauged? Had it not gone before it was alienated? What of the economic law of diminishing return of sexual excitement? What of the law of survival of the fittest? What of good old-fashioned rugged individualism and cut-throat competition?

Slowly and without much public comment or concern the public attitude toward bastardy is being liberalized. The last century has witnessed an active and sustained effort both in this country and abroad to raise the civil status and rights of illegitimate children, including the advocacy of their complete legitimation under various circumstances. Legislation is prevalent legitimating the issue of void or annulled marriages, adopting the civil law principles of legitimation by subsequent matrimony, creating rights of intestate succession between the illegitimate child and its mother, and conferring rights on the child and correlative duties and obligations upon the father. In many instances the illegitimate child is placed exactly on the same par with legal issue for all purposes, including rights of inheritance, and rights to name. Even to remove whatever social stain may attach to illegitimacy, legislation has been passed to shield the child from this stigma. New York, Massachusetts and North Carolina require that the record of adoption proceedings need not disclose whether the child was legitimate or not. While under the common law a bastard had no rights of inheritance from its mother, prevailing American legislation recognizes the relation between mother and child to approximate the status of that of lawful parent and child.

While the incident of inheritance is most important, the other rights of custody, guardianship, apprenticeship and adoption are also recognized. Numerous statutes have been passed legitimating a child with respect to its father. The Civil Law Rule of Legitimation by subsequent marriage has been adopted extensively and many states have even recognized legitimation where there has been no subsequent marriage. In a number of states, including Alabama, Georgia, Mississippi, North Carolina, Tennessee, legitimation may be effected through judicial proceedings by a petition and decree which results in conferring upon the child all rights and privileges of the natural child and giving to it the name of its father. In some states more informal methods are provided facilitating legitimation. These statutes are the best evidence of the modern and unmistakable trend toward legitimation and toward the removal of all distinctions both legal and social between illegitimate and legitimate children.

The basic difficulty in all laws that relate to sex expression is the fundamental confusion as between the state and the individual. Quiet, unobstrusive fornication between adults voluntarily entered into may, or may not, be a satisfying and an enriching experience. The mouths of the fornicators surely should be sealed against protest. Now steps in the state and claims that it is injured. I have read statistics showing charts of weakened strains allegedly arising from extra or pre-marital sexual relations. While their validity is doubtful, these data are presented by those who argue for a society wrapped in a chastity belt. They are never really subscribed to by the senators or legislators or judges who add new sections to the penal laws. I wonder if the present Chief Justice of the United States Supreme Court, when he signed his name, as Governor, to the adultery statute of the State of New York, had any other approach to that subject than a general mood of morality, a hope of keeping the family institution in existence in its olden fashion and a willingness to sign even an ineffective and inoperative addition to our then already overburdened list of high crimes and misdemeanors.

This country, which has adhered so doggedly to a worship of the profit motive in life, has been most vigorous in condemnation of profit motive when it impinges on sexual conduct. The numerous statutes concerned with prostitution and indictable acts, by men and women in connection therewith, are primarily aimed against the promotion of commercialized vice—intercourse for profit. The following types of statutes indicate an intent focused upon the profit element of such activity: Pandering and white slave enactments including importing or transporting a woman for the purpose of prostitution, accepting the earnings of the prostitute, operating and maintaining a place or conveyance for the purpose of prostitution, aiding and abetting prostitution, frequenting a house of prostitution, consenting to a wife's remaining in a house of prostitution, procuring a woman to leave home to go to a place or to leave or enter the State for prostitution, etc.

Because the taint is not the sexual act but the act plus money, discrimination against the female has developed in this portion of the law. Unlike our jurisprudence in respect to bribery, where giver and taker are equally guilty, in prostitution cases the male is indeed rarely arrested, but the woman convicted. Armed as we are with a male police force, the dishonest enforcement of such a one-way law is constantly subjected to criticism and it is time that it was changed.

The state should withdraw as a strictly negating influence. Here is a modest program to start with. Let us revert to the freedom of the Founding Fathers of our Nation: abolish all censorship laws. Legalize abortions under medical supervision and within such varying time limits as an increasingly wise and freed medical profession may determine to be safe. Cancel the laws against the spread of birth control information. Repeal the adultery laws. Likewise, the laws against fornication. Abolish the Mann Act except for cases of compulsory and real white slavery.

Do away with all alienation of affection and breach of promise of marriage actions. Liberalize divorce. (Although this book deals with the unmarried adult, it must be noted that those who are most interested and concerned with divorce are those who intend and believe in marriage.) Re-examine all those laws not intended, but now invoked, to impress a stigma of unworthiness on homosexual persons. Stop using in any statutes all such subjective, indefinable terms as lust, lewd, lascivious and indecent. For, above all else, the greatest indecency in life is the perpetuation of ignorance.

So much for clearing the slate. That would be a beginning and one of real significance, particularly in the important widening of the avenues of knowledge, of satisfactory sexual expression and the removal of untold misery due to inadequate knowledge of contraceptives. But beyond this program the law should proceed affirmatively to do penance for the impress of misery which it has left on the sexual lives of our people. Clinics for guidance, for advice, and for the eradication of the shame and guilt motifs should be instituted. A live jurisprudence should construct an affirmative pattern to develop an adjusted people living with taste in every emotional adventure.

# MORALS

> Where there is mutual freedom and no pecuniary motive, love is good; where these conditions fail, it may often be bad. It is because they fail so frequently in the conventional marriage that a morality which is positive rather than restrictive, based upon hope rather than fear, is compelled, if it is logical, to disagree with the received code in matters of sex.—BERTRAND RUSSELL.

## SEX MORALS AND THE UNMARRIED ADULT

*Horace M. Kallen*
PROFESSOR OF PHILOSOPHY,
NEW SCHOOL FOR
SOCIAL RESEARCH

SO INWARD is the traditional connection between sexual conduct and morality that, for the daily life, usage makes them interchangeable. They lead "moral" lives who conform to the prevailing code of sexual behavior. Rarely is any person called "immoral" because he cheats, steals or murders; but let him be guilty of sexual "misconduct"—fornication, adultery, pederasty or any other unlegalized sex-relationship—and he is also guilty of "immorality."

No female of the species is counted among "the frail sisterhood" or classed as "a fallen woman" or "an erring sister" or "a bad lot" because she has broken some law designed to protect persons, property or contracts. She comes under these categories only if she has "lost her virginity" by "sinning" with somebody not legally her husband or if her behavior otherwise fails to conform to the prevailing conventions of sexual conduct for respectable women. She is then "a light woman," "a wanton," "a loose character," "of easy virtue;" "she has lost her honor" and is "no better than she should be." A man in analogous circumstances is hardly more than a "gay deceiver." If, however, "his intentions are honorable," he marries the lady and thus "does right" by her, "makes an honest woman of her."

Usage establishes "virginity" and "innocence" as practically interchangeable terms. Both, together with their near-synonyms "honor," "chastity" and "purity" stand for valuables which either sex, but the female especially, can only *lose* (even when they are forced and raped; even when it happens on the lawful marriage bed). *Per contra,* just as the statement that a man is "a good husband and father" is employed to condone and to overrule his unethical record in politics, business or other non-sexual walks of life, so alleging that a female is a "good woman,"—i.e., one whom her peers esteem as not violating the prevailing sexual code—is invoked to condone and mollify the acerbities of a difficult personality. As a rule it is the "bad lot" who is described, also, as the "good sort."

Now usage is a matter of class and income, of place and race, of time and circumstances. "Good use" sets up an invidious distinction. It is opposed against "vulgar use," slang and the like; especially against "vulgar use." It designates what is correct speech for people with a certain social inheritance, certain possessions, a certain training, and certain pretensions. It is the linguistic aspect of their mores. Its taboos and prescriptions make a rhyming echo of the taboos and prescriptions which compose their moral code. In certain characteristic ways they are the depository and conservators of that code, paramount instruments of its projection into the future, a dominant item in the social environs of the coming generations. What is correct to say for any given class at any given time reveals what is proper for its members to do and not to do.

In the relations between the sexes this propriety is a thing of peculiarly delicate balance. Its determinants derive from all the institutional interests and personal passions which compose the non-sexual life. They contribute the prescriptive rite and formal ceremony in which correct sexual behavior consists. They lay down the gradients along which instinctive animal impulsion grows into human habit; they enchannel and impattern the sexual energies into the personal relationships whose clash and confluence have been so largely the theme of all the arts. From infancy to second childhood their intent is chiefly restrictive and inhibitory. They ordain little and forbid much.

Seen from the standpoint of personal well-being or social welfare, there is no reason in them. Their beginning was perhaps the discovery and holding in mind of the rôle of the father in procreation. The incest-taboos, which the psychoanalysts designate as the Œdipus complex, may have been consequences of this discovery, and from these the patriarchate and the universal religion of the Phallus may have had their start. Although the anthropologists and the archeologists differ widely here, the consensus seems to be that pre-patriarchal societies knew neither incest nor chastity. Since the relation of mother to child is as certain as such things can be, while that of the father to child is far more a matter of faith than of knowledge, the primary incest-taboos may have been established and chastity and virginity may have been imposed on the female as forms—to use an expression of Alfred Adler's—of "the masculine protest" of the male against his inferiority relationship to the children. Like the *couvade,* they may have been devised to establish as his property the fruit of the womb. Upon this successful struggle of the male for supremacy, a success which reaches its ultimate in the Roman *patria potestas,* much of the institutional development of civilization is postulated. Family, church, state, industry, war, art, law and education are associative establishments governed by codes which endeavor both explicitly and implicitly to support the primacy of the male and to protect paternal power from the decline to which it was subject from the moment of its attainment.

Even at its height, in the most completely patriarchalized communities, this establishment was local, limited and characteristic rather of the ruling classes of a community than of the aggregate of its members. Among the populace the patriarchal code could be only an invidious standard, to some degree contaminating the Many from above, but appropriate rather to patrician landlords and warriors than to plebeian artisans and slaves. Nor, in the eyes of the masters, did the code apply to the inferior ranks; it was operative only for the women of their own rank, in their own community; it did not extend to other classes, races, vocations or cults. To date, prostitutes continue to be drawn from the servants and the poor. Mistresses are another story.

Religion, which is the traditional sanction and supporter of morality, repeats and confirms these distinctions of class and rank. Although, in any existing cult, various strata of the social geology are commingled and contemporary with one another, it is possible to distinguish the levels in their order and to design the evolutionary span between eo-religious and neo-religious ideas and practices. At all levels, physiological sexuality is a central fact; and on all levels, rite, ceremony, and liturgy are implicated in a magical employment and mystic projection of sexual energies by means of symbols reshaped from sexual organs, experiences and activities. Almost invariably, the religion of the populace stems from a matriarchal root. Even where its symbols have become phallic, its ritual is orgiastic and its content is fertility, increase, the fullness of the life more abundant. It seeks and sanctifies not the Right, but the Good. The religion of the classes is patriarchal and concerned more with conserving than with getting. Not less sexual than that of the masses, it is more disciplined and withdrawn; it is the religion of possession rather than of need; it seeks and sanctifies not the Good but the Right. The difference affirms itself everywhere—among the Semites, among the Greeks, and among the Romans [1]—in the same way.

In antiquity religion existed as a confederation of cults, a sort of theological and ecclesiastical internationale whose members, although engaged in a competitive struggle for survival with one another, acknowledged the equal claim of each upon survival. By and large, they had in common the affirmation of life, whether in terms of Right or of Good. They accepted sex as they accepted hunger, and all ages lived accordingly. If any were forbidden this natural and humane

[1] Compare Robertson Smith: *The Religion of the Semites;* Gilbert Murray: *Four Stages of Greek Religion;* A. E. Crawley: *The Mystic Rose;* Jane Harrison: *Prolegomna to the Study of Greek Religion;* J. G. Frazer: *The Golden Bough;* H. M. Kallen: *Why Religion.*

self-acquiesence, it was the women of the ruling classes, and they never easily nor quite successfully.

But for obscure reasons antiquity became tired of life. A deadly fatigue developed, a discouragement, slow, long drawn-out, cumulative, which Gilbert Murray aptly describes as "the failure of nerve." This failure registered itself in the decay of the civil and military establishments of the Roman Empire; in the attainment by Christianism to the hegemony over competitive cults, in its expropriation of its competitors' material goods as well as their rituals, symbols and dogmas, which were absorbed into the miraculous manifold of Christian teaching. The theme and burden of this teaching was self-denial, not self-acquiescence; the mortification, not the discipline of the flesh. It still propounded the Good and the Right, but the Good was not of this world which is evil, and the Right was the rejection of this evil world.

The focus of the evil, according to Christianism, was sexuality; salvation from the evil was *askesis* and the essence of *askesis* is the denial, the repression, the extirpation of sexuality. Since, in a man's world with a patriarchal tradition, the carrier of sexuality is woman, woman, as Genesis set forth, was of the devil; Evil was only an emanation of Eve. Thus, by intent, the Christian code made a conflict the very center of every Christian soul. Existence was distorted into a struggle to maintain an impossible code; impossible alike, as the tale of sacerdotal celibacy shows, to the ecclesiastical hierarchy who charged themselves with the profitable business of enforcement, and to the populace who paid for liberty from the other-worldly penalties of deviating from it. Until well after the Counter Reformation, the church condoned and compromised with the sexual actualities of human nature. Carrier of the tradition of antiquity, she retained and employed the pagan affirmations in and through sexuality as well as the Christian denials. In Mary, God's Virgin Mother, the church tended the pagan goddess of fertility and new birth as a foil and counterweight to Christ, God's son, the Christian divinity of dearth and painful death. It is Mary, not Christ, who rules in the hearts of the Catholic masses, and they worship, besides, patron saints of love and of begetting. In fact, the religion of *askesis,* of repression and denial, failed to penetrate the folkways of the peoples of Europe. It merely modified the formulation of their mores; it imposed upon them a new language and established one more barrier to the winning of increase, of the life more abundant whose symbols derive from sexuality. They lived and loved freely as heretofore. It was the patricians, rather than the populace of Europe, who usually came under the yoke of the Christian code. And they came under it because it carried the patriarchal premise which begot it to the logical limit, transforming chastity, purity, virginity and the like from worldly security for the honor and prestige of the father into the other-worldly conditions of heavenly felicity for the child, more specifically for the female child. That it thereby also enabled the child to free itself from the paternal bondage is a secondary though significant consequence; for women, especially, the nunnery was usually asylum and escape from much worse, and often it was freedom, sexual and otherwise.

The Protestant Reformation, which enabled the clergy to change their status, if they so wished, from unmarried to married adults, at the same time shifted the burden of purity and continence to the unmarried laity. It also threw the responsibility for his sin upon the person himself, depriving him at one fell swoop of confession, penance and absolution. Unlike the Roman Catholic, a Protestant, more particularly a Calvinist, who became sullied could not be cleansed. Both by inheritance and by acquirement he was a miserable sinner, with a conscience agonized, because not unburdened, over his parlous Total Depravity and Original Sin. Artisan and trader, accumulating power because he saved and produced while his noble rulers consumed and spent, his commercial thrift overflowed his personal life, and his sexual behavior became as parsimonious and calculated as his vocational. Since he actually exalted purity, it became a game of his country's gentlemen to degrade it. Men—*vide* Pepys, *vide* the Elizabethan drama in all its ranges and levels—began to identify their honor largely with the exclusive monopoly of their wives' favors. To avoid being cuckolded oneself and to cuckold others, especially tradesmen and solid citizens, was a generation's ruling sport. Wives and daughters, it was believed, were weak, frail creatures, unable to resist the blandishments of any male of gentle blood. Their chastity and virginity, as the repositories of the husband's or the father's honor, must be guarded by all sorts of devices—from segregation to constant chaperonage, which, of course, was costly.

During the 18th century, the gentleman's code for gentlemen contaminated the commoners. At the same time, the gentleman gave up discipline, gave up the attainment of right conduct. The Right, and the disciplines which are implied by any idea of Right, became the moral standard of the merchant and craftsman. The nobleman assimilated himself, so far as his enjoyment of the liberty and security of free income permitted, to the populace in pursuing the Good. Chastity became a prerogative of the middle class.

The 19th century is the century of this middle class. Its dominant era is called Victorian. From the point of view of the mores of sex, it is, other things being equal, the century *par excellence* of prudery, sentimentalism and hypocrisy. Genteel Victoria is its just symbol and incarnation. Tennyson's *The Princess* and *Idylls of the King* set forth both its code and its aspirations. But other things were not equal. The 19th century was *par excellence* also the century of democracy, of science and of industry, of the gathering of tremendous populations into great cities, of the spread of free public education and of the development of feminism. These forces dissolved the homogeneity of the middle class, separating it into grades—upper, lower and many more—and into racial, vocational, religious and national groups. Heir of the patriarchal code of sex-conduct though this class had become, its component groups were themselves too parvenu, too uncertain in the patriarchal rôle to be able to shut off its views and attitudes from contamination by all these innovative influences.

This contamination begins the dissolution of the patriarchal sex mores in their remaining citadel. To the sex-ways of the now rapidly urbanizing populace the changes made little difference. The spontaneous and open information of the country were replaced by the involuntary and half-hidden discoveries of the crowded city-dwelling. A new language developed but, in the main, the patterns of sex-behavior continued to be those of the basic folkways passed on from antiquity—intrinsically without sin, without shame and free.

In America they are seen at their most characteristic among Negroes, urban equally with rural. Where, for tangent causes not intrinsically connected with sexuality, the agonized conscience became a part of the tradition of daily life, for example, among some sects of the Pennsylvania Dutch, or sections of the southern poor whites, the habits based on the crumbling *patria potestas* persist substantially the same, unchanged. Among the Dutch it was the contamination of the whole emotional life by the passion for thrift; among the poor whites, it was the confrontation with the Negroes, so nearly their cultural and economic equals. The one way in which their inferiority could be unequivocally manifested and maintained was for the white male to have free access to the black female, but to deny the white female to the black male. "The honor of southern womanhood" thus became the name for an invidious distinction compensating a deep and widespread feeling of inferiority and sense of guilt which placates itself periodically by lynchings and burnings. To these emotions, economic passions are at first only contributory; later they become paramount. "The honor of southern womanhood," then, rationalizes the endeavor to keep the slowly but surely escaping Negro available for exploitation. In other respects, as the novels of Erskine Caldwell indicate, within the slight dams of the Christian code, the old pagan sex-ways prevail in the South. And, indeed, in the North and the East and the West. And why should they not?

The subjection of women, which is the turning point of sex-ways in a man's world, is a social, not a biological fact. Maybe it is true that females are more anabolic than males and males more katabolic than females, and it is plausible that this difference of energic equilibrium may follow from an inbalance which the addition or subtraction of a single chromosome may determine.

But no convincing parallels can be brought of female subjection in the animal or insect worlds. On the contrary, the actuality is somewhat the reverse. It is true that for coitus the male mounts the female; and, indeed, Alfred Adler has built an imposing psychological structure upon the event, making use of "inferiority feelings," "masculine protests" and such concepts for materials. There is nothing, however, in either the psychophysics of sexuality or the history of sex-ways to warrant the inference that the sexual subjection of women follows inevitably from the nature of things, a foregone conclusion from "evolution," "dialectics of matter" or "will of God." It can hardly be said that among the masses of men whose lives are always lived close to the level of subsistence there is, or ever has been, a double standard. The poor have little or no access to the surrogates for what the mother of a very distinguished British critic's seven-year-old offspring once labeled to me as "the coarser pleasures." Few of the arts and the amenities are within their reach. They are sweated to the point of fatigue and dullness in the cotton factories of Carolina and Georgia, in the shirt factories of Pennsylvania, and the dress factories and offices of Ohio and Michigan and New York. They have their religion, of course. But for many Protestants, the height of religion is the orgiastic revival meeting; and the Roman Catholic can sin and repent and be absolved, and sin again. For both, as for all, sex is the great renewer, sexual excitement the great vitalizer.

On the whole, the conscience, agonized over changing sex-ways—over the conflict set up between inborn impulsions, natural attitudes and habits, and acquired doctrines, is a function of the intellectual rather than of the moral climate. It registers itself earliest and prophetically in the views of such spirits as Shelley, Godwin, Mary Wollstonecraft, Stuart Mill and his wife, George Meredith, the Socialists and the makers and leaders of the woman's movement. It is a cerebral, not a spinal view. Its teachings are peculiarly humanitarian, external and unphysiologic, a sexless affirmation of the equal freedom of the sexes, addressed to men and women equally cerebral and equally agonized over sex. Only when the 19th century is well into its last quarter are the social and humanitarian preoccupations supplemented by the psychophysiological, the anthropological and the clinical. Iwan Bloch, Mantegazza, Krafft-Ebing, Magnus Hirschfeld, Edward Carpenter, Havelock Ellis and Freud publish discussions and analyses that first shock, then intrigue, then persuade the educated, middle-class world.

Erotica there had always been but never before such erotica as these moderns. They compose a new and unprecedented integer of intellectual culture. They set sex in a different dimension and its ways in untraditional patterns. But most certainly it is not the sex and the sex-ways of the masses they so set. The ways and thoughts of peasants and workers are not their themes. Those are drawn on for argument and illustration; incidental observations, rumors, legends and the like are cited and repeated. But direct empirical observations of the sex-ways of the European Massemensch, comparable to those which anthropologists make of Indians and Negroes and Australians and Eskimos in their native habitat, are still to be reported. Concerning the sex-ways of those remote and alien peoples there is ample observation and comment; also concerning the record of antiquity. But the European and American contemporaries of whom the authorities treat are first and last intellectuals, self-conscious members of a sophisticated minority in whose soul the feeling of moral obligation acquired from their elders wars with the vital tides of the personal libido. More often than not these men and women are people without roots—artists, writers, journalists, teachers, scientists—their training and vocations have dislodged them from the mores of the very class which nurtured them, and have left them without a home in any. Initially, individuals at loose ends and at a loss, they drift together and fall into a way of life of their own. They compose, as do prostitutes and criminals, a sort of marginal class, recruited from all, representative of none, having its own code and mores. But they are a reflective and articulate class and eagerly vocal. They it is who answer the questionnaires, analyze the problems and argue the issues. They were the "flaming youth" and "lost generation" of 1924. They are the patients and correspondents of Drs. Hamilton and Davis, the parents of Ben Lindsay's companionatuses, the eager debaters about the Russian recodification of sex-ways. Among them, also, are the unmarried adults who replied to the questionnaire which I circulated in order to secure a record of their immediate and actual sexual morality.

The ages of those replying range from twenty-one to thirty-four years and the women among them, as is not unusual with sex questionnaires, outnumber the men four to one. Practically all have attended college. They confess to confusion and bewilderment in politics and, except for a couple of Roman Catholics and an atheist, to uncertainty and searching in religion. Most of them admit autoerotic practices and that they have suffered from the customary childhood feelings of shame and awkwardness concerning sex, especially at puberty. Only two manifest the correctly respectable revulsion at the idea of homosexuality; most of them acknowledge "an intellectual interest" in it, and one, sympathy. Half of the women and two-thirds of the men admit intercourse beginning at ages which run from fourteen and one-half to twenty-eight years. Only two-thirds of the women would like to be married and none of the men. Both sexes find their present mode of life inadequate and unsatisfying—not sexually, but socially and hygienically. The women are anxious over the danger of venereal disease and the danger of conception. It is not for love that they desire marriage but for security, companionship and protection, and in several cases, for children. The men are afraid of marriage and of fatherhood; all are afraid of the economic burden of a family and some fear the moral obligation of being faithful to one woman.

What is paramount, from the point of view of morals, is that they deny all feelings of guilt about their sex-ways. Economically insecure, politically confused and intellectually and religiously uncertain though they are, the agonized conscience is conspicuously absent from their psyche. The cross-section of the aggregate of unmarried adults they represent know all about sex and sexuality, its theory and its practice. Not only they, but even their mothers and fathers know what it would be like to grow up in Samoa, and accept the invidious implication for New York. They have read Ellis and Freud, Ellen Key and the Russells; they are familiar with Stopes and with Robey; they know contraceptives, and some have had considerable experience with abortion. They are aware that the "old maid" must be a deteriorated person and they believe that this deterioration is a consequence of continence. A few, indeed, had undergone sex education in high school and had read Mary Ware Dennett's pamphlet as a lesson. Those of their brothers and sisters who attend the progressive schools will receive instruction either through it or an equivalent. The youngest children of their families are being introduced to the sex-ways of their race and class by means of such books as Karl de Schweinitz's *Growing Up;* Emma Gillmore's *The Why and How of Life;* Frances Bruce Strain's *New Patterns in Sex Teaching.* Not only do they discuss sex and sex-ways more freely with each other than their parents did at the same age but they discuss them with their parents, with their mothers more readily than with their fathers, for even mothers, they have learned, remain women and share with women the more personal stake in a reformed code of sexual morality. The sons and daughters frankly accept even smut and enjoy hearing and telling salacious stories—"if they are funny"—in mixed company.

All in all, the standards of the educated middle class are shifting—because of the flow of influence from their uprooted scions forming a new, marginal class—toward the standards of the populace. They tend to affirm sex education, birth control, freedom for the unmarried, easy marriage and easy divorce, and the personal ineffability and privacy of sexual union; as girls keep asserting, "If I want to, it's nobody's business but my own." Neither sex makes much of *right* and *wrong* as their moral measures. Like the pre-Christian world and the Christian populace they seek the Good. The questions they raise are, "What have I to gain or lose in accepting or abandoning the traditional sex-ways? Shall I be hurt or helped?" Constant with the girl is the fear of being hurt—not so much through pregnancy or venereal infection, as through loss of status, not so much in the eyes of the community as in the eyes of her lover. "Will he respect me? Will he think I'm easy?" is a not infrequent thought in the mind of a girl ready to change her condition to the last one beyond technical virginity. And, in many instances, if the lovers' reports are veracious, they are at last put to the question, and find it difficult to give an honest answer. These fears add to whatever potency remains in the patriarchal code for women.

But they are not enough. The trend in the middle class toward sex-ways grounded on the psychophysical actualities of our sexual nature is strong and gathering momentum, and in another generation all of its groups should be conducting themselves knowingly and with conscious intention even as the populace conduct themselves spontaneously and without purpose. Dr. G. V. Hamilton points out that whereas of a group of married women whose sex life he studied only twenty-four per cent of those born between 1886 and 1890 had illicit relations before marriage, sixty-one per cent of those born between 1891 and 1895 had such relations. With the college and high-school girls of the present decade the ratio increases. Significantly, however, this does not mean that legal marriage decreases. On the contrary. Recently Dr. Charles W. Margold completed a lengthy, unfortunately still unpublished, statistical study of the frequency of marriages between spinsters and bachelors, the divorced and the widowed. His survey embraces a period of some fifty to seventy-five years and counts a billion and a half marriages in fifty-four countries, including the United States, jointly and severally. It also distinguishes metropolitan and rural areas. Dr. Margold found that everywhere first marriages are increasing absolutely and relatively; that both men and women are marrying younger than they once did—this holding true more for the men than the women; that religious and ethnic lines are being disregarded, especially among Roman Catholics and Jews. As Anatole France said somewhere: "*Chacun fait son salut comme il peut.*"

If the record indicates anything, it indicates that the morals of sex are a mystery. Whatever salvation any individual accomplishes, he accomplishes in his own way, according to his own pattern. Its materials and conditions consist of his community, its mores, and its ruling passions. They constitute both his limitations and his opportunities, nor is there anything else for him to work with. His sex-ways will follow one channel if he is a peasant, another if he is an industrial worker, or a tradesman, or a gentleman, or a banker, or a soldier, or a sailor, or a Protestant, or a Roman Catholic, or a clergyman, or an artist, or a politician, or an engineer, or a Fascist, or a Communist or an anarchist. His church, his nationality, his country, his local habitation, his reading, the condition of the national and local economy, the rivalry and conflict between the groups, classes and sects composing his community, the ratio of the sexes to each other and the state of the industrial arts—all will be factors. The one perennial constant in the determination of sex-ways is the physiological organism with its mechanisms and their developmental dynamic. The rest, the essence and form of the psychological personality, gets its movement and pattern from the facilitations and obstructions presented by the total environment to which it is responsive. It shapes itself from what it assimilates, what it conforms to, what it withdraws from and what it rejects. Changes in these make changes in the sex-ways. A personality, indeed, is but the process and form of interaction between the physiological *homo sapiens* and this labile nexus of social recapitulation and social innovation in which he lives and moves and has his being.

The moral validity of the process, the excellence of the form—insofar as there can be excellence and moral validity—are neither intrinsic nor static. They consist in consequences; and to have consequences, form and process must not be self-constricting or self-defeating; they must not dam themselves up from within nor cut themselves off from without. *Integer vitae,* the feeling of the freedom and abundance of life, are conditioned upon open ways to this self-balancing confluence of individual idiosyncrasy and social forces. Where these ways lie and of what they are made cannot be told in advance; they vary with each civilization and each generation, from community to community, and individual to individual, and none can say for another when or under what configuration of circumstances he shall feel with this feeling. When it lives in him, he is an open personality to himself, and an open way to others: his mood and tonus irradiate all within reach with their quality. When he lacks it, he is a personality shut-in, self-obstructed within, blocked and blocking without. That the intensity, manner and direction of his sexual life plays a prepotent rôle in the formation and flow of his personality, is now a commonplace among the intellectuals. But whether openness depends upon indulgence or continence, profligacy or celibacy, gratification or sublimation, *laissez faire* or social control, who can tell? How choose between a St. Francis and a Goethe, a Swinburne and a Darwin, a Shelley and a Spinoza?

Among women, parallels as conspicuous are lacking,

alas, for obvious but now happily obsolescent reasons. It is not, as Havelock Ellis thinks, and as Bertrand Russell thinks, together with the whole present generation of liberal intellectuals, that sexual union is not a social act and that sexual morality revolves round the child. It is, that sexual union, whether ineffably secret or heedlessly public—and it happens both ways—has consequences other than children for the individuals who enter into it and through them for the whole world of humans with whom they are in living contact. This is why a child is no less private than the union which generates it and the union no less social than the child which may be one of its consequences. There are many and varied channels for the sexual energies, and the human, *qua* human, are only contingently the physiological channels. Freedom is not the autonomy and self-sufficiency of the present moment; it is the enriching flow of personality into future abundance. In some communities a maximum of regulation may facilitate this, in others a minimum, with all the degrees between. Which does, in any instance, only the experimental event can decide.

To date, the issue is still unclosed. It is too soon to draw any objective conclusion from the record of the brave Russian adventure. The first effect of the abrogation of the pre-revolutionary sex-ways and the ordination of the Communist code was a literal carrying out of Havelock Ellis' doctrines *(Studies in the Psychology of Sex;* Vol. VI, *Sex in Relation to Society, p. 417.)*:

Sexual union for a woman as much as for a man, is a physiological fact; it may also be a spiritual fact; but it is not a social act. It is, on the contrary, an act which, beyond all other acts, demands retirement and mystery for its accomplishment. . . . The sexual act is of no more concern to the community than any other private physiological act. It is an impertinence, if not an outrage, to seek to inquire into it. But the birth of a child is a social act. The whole of sexual morality . . . revolves round the child.

The sexual act was evaluated as of no social consequence, as a "private physiological act." An orgiastic interlude ensued which caused considerable anxiety among the revolutionary elders and led Lenin to complain to Clara Zetkin that the sexual interest had displaced all other and many more important ones; that Communism and the Revolution, far from being treated as a goal, were being employed as a means to rationalize promiscuity and "entirely bourgeois" sensuality. A press campaign of admonition and indoctrination followed, and in the course of time, perhaps for other reasons, the sexual excitement relaxed. Currently, observers report that the difference in male and female attitude evinced by the unmarried adult in the United States is apparent also in Russia. Men consciously prefer to manage their sexual relations on the basis of a rational materialism and to confine love to physiological union; women desire love in the older, "bourgeois" sense of the term. Other things being equal, we shall be able to infer, in another generation or two, whether Russia's new sex-ways make for *integer vitae*. Meanwhile, there is no indication that men and women cause each other less misery there than elsewhere.

# LITERATURE

> The novel has this one great counterpoise of undoubted good to set against all the manifold disadvantages and shortcomings of romantic literature—that it always appeals to the true internal promptings of inherited instinct, and opposes the foolish and selfish suggestions of interested outsiders. It is the perpetual protest of poor banished human nature against the expelling pitchfork of calculating expediency in the matrimonial market.—GRANT ALLEN

## THE SEX LIFE OF THE UNMARRIED ADULT IN ENGLISH LITERATURE

*Robert Morss Lovett*
PROFESSOR OF ENGLISH
UNIVERSITY OF CHICAGO

IT SCARCELY need be noted, at the outset, that the sex life of the unmarried adult contributes largely to the themes, incidents, and psychology which make up the substance of English imaginative literature. Indeed, so largely has this source been exploited, so much today are its products taken for granted, that we find a shifting of interest to the sex life of the adolescent and the child. It is indeed a striking mark of modernity that a physical function, with its development into human relations, which was formerly fraught with enormous significance for the individual and society, which was a subject of social and religious penalties of the most terrific import, of which the crises and exigencies were in the highest degree tragic in their consequences, is becoming an accepted commonplace in literature as it is in life.

The importance attached to the sex life of the unmarried adult, shown by the sanctions by which it was surrounded, goes back to the primitive teachings of Christianity and the cult of virginity therein set forth. Specifically the values attached to the subject in modern literature may be referred to the doctrine of romantic love, which became almost a religion in the Middle Ages, and to the revival of Christianity in the Reformation, which in its English form of Puritanism exercised for centuries a profound influence on English manners and character. The romantic relation of man and woman, wherein passion unrewarded is sublimated into an ecstasy of devotion, was necessarily an aristocratic conception at variance with reality but furnishing a convention for poetry and romance, an ideal which finds its exemplification in the story of the troubadour Rudel and the Lady of Tripoli, preserved for our own day in Browning's poem and Rostand's *La Princesse Lointaine.* Reminiscences of this aristocratic idealization of the relation of the sexes are evident in the courtly literature of the Elizabethan Age, in the chivalric attitude of the knights Pyrocles and Musidorus toward the princesses Pamela and Philoclea in Sidney's *Arcadia,* in the celebration of chastity in the Third Book of *The Faerie Queene,* and also in the comedy of manners known as *Euphues.* One of the discussions in *Euphues and His England,* in imitation of the mythical courts of love, concerns the question whether lovers should have the right to meet or not.

On the other hand, the popular literature of Elizabeth's reign reflects the realism of its medieval progenitors in the matter of sex. Especially, the picaresque romance furnished an antitype to the romance of chivalry. In the former, instead of the knight errant setting forth on an ideal quest in behalf of his lady's honor or the Holy Grail, we have a rogue errant, wandering in search of bodily satisfactions, among which sexual gratification played an exciting part. The picaresque romance imported from Spain and the *novella* from Italy constituted the bulk of fiction for the Elizabethan populace. The latter furnished the accepted stuff for the drama of Shakespeare and his successors whose treatment of sex grew more and more uninhibited until the theatres were closed by the Puritans in 1643. Meanwhile, the Spanish rogue excited the competition of English writers. Thomas Nashe in *The Unfortunate Traveller* takes his hero from adolescence to maturity in sexual experience; and in *The English Rogue*, by Kirkman and Head, written in the lush time of the Restoration, the hero patriotically surpasses the exploits of his foreign models, and gives to English sexual adventure, extending even to India, glory truly imperial.

The great difference between the English and the continental view of sexual life was undoubtedly due to the subjection of the former to the principle of continence-until-marriage enforced by Puritanism. In this connection, the case of Milton is important as that of a great poet who in his apostrophe: "Hail, Wedded Love" in *Paradise Lost*, gave expression to a doctrine which remained characteristic of the English theory of morals to the end of the 19th century. Milton as a young man was strongly affected by the beauty of woman, as we may infer from his college letters in Latin verse to his friend, Charles Diodati, and from his sonnets in Italian to an unknown girl whom he knew apparently before his journey to Italy. He had made up his mind, in the interest of his vocation as poet, not to marry; and this resolution carried with it a vow of celibacy. He wrote his masque *Comus* in celebration of "the sage and serious doctrine of virginity," and, if we may take the exposition by the Elder Brother at face value, we may infer that Milton attributed to chastity a certain supernatural power. At all events, in the autobiographical passages scattered throughout his earliest prose pamphlets, on the general theme of church government, we find a constant insistence on his own virginity, and even an argument to prove that if unchastity is reprehensible in a woman, who is only the image of man, it is much more so in man, who is the image of God himself. Somewhere along the way, however, Milton decided to marry, and therefore extends his definition of chastity to include the state of living in wedded bliss. There is in the "Apocalypse" a passage promising to 40,000 saints who have not been defiled with women the special favor of perpetually accompanying the Lamb. Milton angrily combats the notion that this company excludes married men who have kept their vows, "for marriage is no defilement." When his own marriage was broken by the desertion of his wife, Milton took the modern course of reconciling the sanctity of the marriage bond with personal inclination by arguing for free and easy divorce. In his *Doctrine and Discipline of Divorce* there is a plea on behalf of the chaste and continent young man for the legal rectification of mistakes in marriage, couched in the language of personal grievance, which has been echoed by countless successors, the dupes of their own virtue.

The soberest and best governed men are least practiced in these affairs—it is not strange though many, who have spent their youth chastely, are in some things not so quick-sighted, while they haste too eagerly to light the nuptial torch; nor is it, therefore, that for a modest error a man should forfeit so great a happiness, and no charitable means to release him, since they who have lived most loosely, by reason of their bold accustoming, prove most successful in their matches, because their wild affections unsettling at will, have been as so many divorces to teach them experience.

The theological and moral burdens which Puritanism imposed on the English people proved too great for the imagination and the flesh. The reaction which followed the Restoration resulted in one of those periods of licentiousness which, like the Regency in France, have become legendary. The sexual mores of the time are revealed in the memoirs of Count de Grammont, in the fictionized gossip of Mrs. Manley, in the drama of Dryden, Congreve, and Wycherly, in the poetry of Rochester and Sedley. The license of the Restoration brought the inevitable reaction. The Revolution of 1688 was made possible by the support of the middle class, which during the 18th century advanced rapidly in economic and social, if not in political, power, and the middle class in the 18th, as in the 19th century, kept, with compromise, the Puritan faith. The social effort of the writers of the age of Queen Anne was to clean up the moral mess left by the Restoration. There is in Defoe, however, as less obviously in Steele and Addison, evidence of the compromise between Puritan theory and worldly practice which was later a prominent characteristic of Victorianism. The middle class showed itself complacent toward the flagrant vices of the aristocracy. Within itself it demanded the appearance of decency more insistently than its reality. The period became one of shows and shams, denounced in contemporary literature by Swift, and later by Carlyle. In short, the year 1688 marks a compromise which was no less social than political, the effects of which lasted for two hundred years.

There are three authors of the 18th century who are of special interest to us in a study of the sex life of the unmarried adult. The first is Lord Chesterfield, whose letters to his son are a perfect statement of the ideals of modern aristocratic civilization. Lord Chesterfield was concerned to make his son and pupil an accepted man of the world. He therefore recommended a series of intrigues with older and experienced ladies of *ton* as a means of polishing the crudeness of youth, a practice recommended in the novels of aristocratic manners of the early 19th century, notably Bulwer-Lytton's *Pelham.*

The two other figures are, of course, the rival novelists, Richardson and Fielding. Richardson was thoroughly of the middle class; he represented it and entertained it. It is not the least of his middle-class characteristics that he showed himself willing, in his days of fame, to graduate into the ranks of the lower aristocracy where he found many female admirers. His first novel, *Pamela or Virtue Rewarded,* is the story, told by herself, of the attempted seduction of a servant girl by her employer, a certain Mr. B; of her successful resistance, and of the final triumph of her continence in bringing her master to the altar. There is obviously a certain flaw in the morality of the story, an element of calculation in Pamela's maneuvers; and, as Sidney

Lanier remarked, the novel might as well be entitled "Mr. B or the Reward of Vice." Nevertheless, the story was taken at its face value by simple, right-thinking people; and it is related that in one country parish where the vicar read the book aloud to his flock, the triumphant dénouement, when the virtuous Pamela at last renders the rose which she has so valiantly defended to the repentant, reformed, and hereafter complacent Mr. B, was greeted by loud cheers and the ringing of the church bells.

In Richardson's second novel, *Clarissa,* the heroine, of a rich middle-class family, is induced by their persecution to flee from home under the protection of a young aristocrat, Lovelace. Clarissa would marry Lovelace, but is impeded by scruples arising out of the compromising situation which alone makes marriage obligatory. Lovelace would marry Clarissa but is tempted by the pride of the gentleman sportsman to possess without paying the price. After his rape of Clarissa there is nothing left for the heroine but the reward of heaven. The last of Richardson's novels, *Sir Charles Grandison,* is a translation of middle-class morals into aristocratic manners. The hero is a model of continence, postponing his marriage to Miss Harriet Byron until an incredible number of fantastic obligations to others have been fulfilled. Here we have three novels, admittedly works of genius, based upon problems of the sexual relations of unmarried adults, without any precise recognition of the appetite which animates them. Although Pamela is in love with Mr. B, her letters to her parents describing in detail the efforts of the latter to violate her in her bed contain no intimation of an internal struggle with suppressed desires. Her concern is entirely with the technical affair of her virtue; while Mr. B, though registering the behavior of lust, is only the exhibitionist familiar to us on the screen. Similarly, the relation of Clarissa and Lovelace, based on the war of the sexes, is a long-drawn negotiation about the technical matter of marriage. The rape of Clarissa takes place off stage.

The popularity of Richardson's novels, and the number of his imitators, especially women, bear witness to their success in striking the exact note of middle-class sexual morality in the 18th century. His rival was Henry Fielding, an aristocrat who nevertheless confessed that he found low life more interesting, richer in human quality, than respectable society. It was the false morality of Pamela which impelled Fielding to write his burlesque, *Joseph Andrews,* in which Pamela's brother is made the object of attempted seduction by Lady Booby. Fielding's great work, *Tom Jones,* may be called the typical English novel, in its biographical form, its mystery plot turning on the concealed identity of the hero, its explicit characterization, and its inclusion of the essay, permitting free personal communication between the author and his readers. Thanks to the latter quality, we know exactly what Fielding is about. He tells us at the outset that the dish he sets before us is human nature—and human nature includes sex. Tom Jones is a typical young aristocrat. He falls in love with Sophia Western, for whom he does not confess a fleshly desire, and meanwhile solaces himself with the embraces of Molly Seagrim, the daughter of a game-keeper. Persuaded by her that he is the father of her child-to-be, he renounces Sophia in his heart and goes to offer marriage to the girl he has wronged, only to find another in possession of her charms. But this is not the end. Seeking a retired spot to meditate upon his renewed hopes of Sophia, this very preoccupation renders him an easy prey to Molly, returning from her work in the fields, her sex appeal heightened by an "odoriferous effluvia," which modern voluptuaries call body odor. His fall on this occasion causes his exile from his patron's house, and his later seduction in London by Lady Ballaston nearly ruins his cause with Sophia. She, however, like Amelia in Fielding's latest novel, adds to the virtue of chastity that of tolerance, of which both heroes, Tom Jones and Captain Booth, stand in constant need. Fielding's code of sexual morality is that of the aristocrat as opposed to that of the bourgeois Richardson, and is responsible for the robust realism with which he treats the theme. Females of the upper class are by hypothesis virgins before, and faithful wives after, marriage. Their lower class sisters and all men are naturally animals.

The two tendencies represented by Richardson and Fielding, the bourgeois-reticent and the aristocratic-realistic, persisted in the romantic literature of the 19th century. Scott is clearly of the school of Richardson in this matter. Once only in the course of the Waverley novels does he base a situation on premarital sexual indulgence—the case of Effie Deans in *The Heart of Midlothian.* Wordsworth in his long account of the growth of his poetic mind, the *Prelude,* leaves out entirely what must have been both a shattering and a vivifying experience—his love of Annette Vallon and the birth of his illegitimate daughter. On the other hand, Byron made sex a leading theme in his romantic tales and dramas, and based the greatest of them, *Manfred,* on his own incest. In *Don Juan* he wrote for the romantic 19th century what Fielding had written for the realistic 18th—a vivacious narrative of violence and passion, of fighting and fornication. Following the romantic vogue of Scott and Byron, there succeeded a period characterized by the novel of manners, in which the society novel, "silver fork fiction" as it was called, was distinguished for its freedom of treatment of sex, so much so that Bulwer-Lytton expressed grave fears for the future prestige of an aristocracy whose frailties were paraded so freely for the entertainment of the public. On the other hand, it is to be noted that a contemporary school of popular novelists treating low life, even in the vulgar bohemianism of Pierce Egan's *Life in London*, is remarkably free from sexual themes.

It was the reticence of Richardson rather than the robust frankness of Fielding that triumphed in English literature of the Victorian period. So far as the evidence of letters goes, one might infer that the sex life of the unmarried adult was confined to the windy wistfulness, recrimination, and renunciation familiar in Tennyson's *Locksley Hall* and *Maud*, or to the Miltonic idealism of the *Princess*. In this respect literature addressed the middle class, which supplied a new and enormous reading public, whose philistinism was a degradation of Puritanism into what Grant Allen described as "that national moral blight that calls itself respectability."

It must not be inferred, however, that the disappearance of sex from Victorian literature was entirely, or even chiefly, due to the impulse to cover up. In the first place there was a genuine revival of religion. The Methodist revival of the 18th century appealed largely to a class below the level of literature, but the Oxford Movement of the 1830's, which merged into the Anglo-Catholic Movement, and the Evangelical Movement, with its offshoot, the Broad Church Movement, took place among the cultivated classes, affecting even the aristocracy. The religious novels written in such numbers by Miss Charlotte M. Yonge, from the Anglo-Catholic point of view, by Miss Mulock, Mrs. Oliphant, George Macdonald and William Hale White, from the evangelical or liberal, undoubtedly appealed to a public to which sex had become a minor interest, its claims amply satisfied by marriage, whose sacramental character precluded Milton's doctrine of divorce. Marriage was the foundation of the home, which to the Victorians constituted the basis of a practical six-day-a-week religion—the "pure religion breathing household laws" of Wordsworth. It is noteworthy how the religious and domestic themes are combined in the minor but very popular fiction of the 19th century, such as *John Halifax, Gentleman,* and the poems of Mrs. Hemans. (*The Graves of the Household, The Homes of England,* etc.) Springing out of the religious interest is the theme of renunciation, powerfully reënforced by the eloquence of Carlyle. It would be hard to say to what extent this form of 19th century idealism is due to the famous passages in *Sartor Resartus,* based on a perhaps wilful misunderstanding of Goethe. At all events, the poetry and fiction of the Victorian period is full of examples of self-sacrifice in the matter of sexual satisfaction, sacrifice to the claims of family, of faith, even of rivals. The great dramatic scenes of Victorian fiction are scenes of renunciation—Sidney Carton's in *A Tale of Two Cities,* Henry Esmond's, Maggie Tulliver's. No one will doubt the sincerity of the great Victorian novelists in these scenes, but it is equally beyond doubt that their contemporaries, perplexed in regard to the solution of a triangle problem, found renunciation on the part of someone a useful resource. The moral bunk which gathered about renunciation was exposed by

Robert Browning in *The Statue and the Bust*, a poem which the Victorians had some difficulty in understanding and accepting.

Certain peculiarities in the Victorian literary conception of sex challenge a brief consideration. Although we have seldom any formal statement of incontinency on the part of young men and women, nevertheless babies are constantly turning up to haunt unmarried mothers—Effie Deans, in Scott's *Heart of Midlothian*, Lady Dedlock, in Dickens' *Bleak House*, Hetty Sorrel, in George Eliot's *Adam Bede*. The last is a rather daring example of realism for its time in its account of the relations of Arthur Donnithorne, the young master of the manor, and his pretty dependent. In a surprising number of cases we are given to understand that the stern judgment, the wages of sin is life, is enforced after a first and single offense, and this offense is attenuated by the ignorance of at least one of the parties as to the meaning and results of the sexual act, an ignorance amounting to innocence. In spite of these apologetics, Victorian writers make no abatement of the furious resentment, amounting to outlawry, with which society pursued the female unmarried sexual offender, for even among the neo-Puritans the double standard as exemplified in *Tom Jones* was perforce accepted. In the ignorance of precautions, the absence of contraceptives, and the lack of standing of abortion in sound medical practice, the usual solution of the problem child is infanticide.

A striking exception, however, is found in Mrs. Gaskell's *Ruth*, which, though dated 1853, deserves credit for anticipating certain developments which are regarded as exclusively modern. Ruth, a milliner's apprentice, like most Victorian heroines, is entirely ignorant of sexual procedure, and falls an innocent victim to a man who leaves her with child. Instead of abortion, infanticide or abandonment, she decides to bear and rear the infant. In this decision she is aided and abetted by the minister of a dissenting chapel, and, with some reluctance, by his sister. This is not the only departure from the code of the age. A most important article of that code, in force from before the time of *Pamela*, to the effect that marriage atones for whatever irregularity of behavior may have preceded it, is deliberately flouted when the man turns up years later, rich and distinguished, and wishes to marry Ruth and assume the paternity of his boy. Ruth refuses on the ground that she does not love him, and does not wish to submit her son to his influence.

Two distinguished novelists of the Victorian era demand special consideration. Thackeray was the heir of the aristocratic tradition of Fielding, whom he accepted as his model. In *Pendennis* he undertook to draw the character and career of a young man of his own day, but in the preface he laments the limitations to which he was obliged to conform.

> Since the author of "Tom Jones" was buried, no writer of fiction among us has been permitted to depict to the utmost of his power a MAN. We must drape him, and give him a certain conventional simper. Society will not tolerate the Natural in Art. Many ladies have remonstrated and subscribers left me, because, in the course of the story, I described a young man resisting and affected by temptation. My object was to say that he had passions to feel, and the manliness and generosity to overcome them.

The episode referred to is Pendennis' flirtation with

a girl of a lower class, Fanny Bolton, in the account of which there is certainly no intimation of anything like passion on his part, although it might be inferred that he was not above accepting a proffered pleasure. It was to clear up any ambiguity on this score, and to restore his hero and himself to the good graces of his readers, that later in the story Thackeray explicitly states that Pendennis' relations with Fanny were technically pure.

The other case in point is that of Charlotte Brontë. The story of the three sisters, in their Yorkshire parsonage, has been told in biography and fiction as a typical example of Victorian repression. We know, from recently published letters, that Charlotte during her stay at Mme. Héger's pension in Brussels to learn French fell desperately in love with M. Héger. After her return to England, when her letters to him were rationed, she fell back on fiction for consolation, her first immature novel, *The Professor,* and her last, *Villette,* being based on this experience. Miss Brontë's first successful novel, *Jane Eyre,* begins with a realistic account of life at school, reminiscent of that of Charlotte and her sisters, but she soon leaves the world of her experience for that of her desires, and creates the romance of Mr. Rochester. The genuine passion which Jane Eyre feels and expresses for this hero, though sanctified by renunciation when she discovers that he is married, was the ground for the condemnation of the book by Lady Eastlake, in the *Quarterly Review,* as unfit for feminine readers. It is in *Shirley,* however, that Miss Brontë's bitterness appears most clearly against a society which leaves its virgins to suffer without means of realizing their desires.

A lover masculine can speak and urge explanation, a

lover feminine can say nothing: if she did the result would be shame and anguish, inward remorse for self-treachery. . . . Take the matter as you find it: ask no questions; utter no remonstrances: it is your best wisdom. You expected bread, and you have got a stone; break your teeth on it, and don't shriek because the nerves are martyrized: do not doubt that your mental stomach—if you have such a thing—is strong as an ostrich's—the stone will digest.

It must not be thought that the Victorians' reticence on the subject of sex was due to lack of interest or feeling. On the contrary, the very taboos and inhibitions by which they surrounded sexual love and its consummation show their reverence for it. That a great love could sanctify life is the burden of Tennyson's and of Browning's poetry. Such a love led through purity to marriage, which was both a sacrament and a mystery, too sacred for even the most reverent art. Coventry Patmore's *The Angel in the House* was looked at askance, and Rossetti for his lovely *House of Life* was brutally denounced by Robert Buchanan for bringing his nuptial couch into the street. It is noteworthy that such regrettable sexual lapses as are admitted into literature are, on the part of the woman, the result of genuine passion or protest against intolerable tyranny—in any case, a recognition of the monogamous standard. Seldom do we find promiscuity accepted, never approved. In Dickens we have, handled discreetly, several cases of women who go wrong–Edith Dombey, Louise Gradgrind, Lady Dedlock, Little Em'ly–but they all bear witness to the belief in the power of love to sanctify or rectify life. It is the loss of the sense of sanctity and mystery, which guard sexual relations, that constitutes the great difference in this matter between the literature of the Victorian Age and our own.

The change in the attitude toward romantic love, which largely determined the sex life of the unmarried adult of the middle class in the Victorian Age, was brought about by the agencies of science and its literary concomitant, realism. With the former we have little concern in this article except to remark that the studies of sexual behavior by Krafft-Ebing, Havelock Ellis, Freud and Jung had a powerful influence on fiction in the twentieth century. Earlier than this, however, the example of continental naturalism in its effort to give a complete, objective and impartial account of human behavior had brought the British public face to face with the question of the limitation of the material of literature in the interest of what was called good taste. This battle was waged fiercely in the decade of 1890. The dramatic critics fought to ban Ibsen from the London stage, and Ernest Vizetelly, the translator and publisher of Zola, was sent to prison. A popular diatribe entitled *Degeneration*, by Max Nordau, made realism one of its chief indictments against modernism, and the first number of *The Yellow Book* contained an impassioned defence, by Arthur Waugh, of "Reticence in Literature."

One of the first offenders against Victorian good taste was Thomas Hardy. In *Tess of the D'Urbervilles* (1890) he defends his heroine, seduced by her master, and mother of an illegitimate child, as a "pure woman," and in scathing pages excoriates the hypocrisy of Angel Clare, who, while asking pardon for his own incontinence, refuses to absolve his wife. Hardy followed this challenge by *Jude the Obscure* (1895), in which almost for the first time in reputable English fiction since the

18th century we have an explicit recognition of the sexual urge. Jude Fawley's ambition is intellectual. He hopes to transcend his condition of workingman by training his mind. He falls victim to the flesh, first by the vulgar seduction of Arabella; again by the more exquisite temptation of Sue Bridehead. These two books revealed Hardy as the greatest living writer of fiction in English, but their reception by the public ended prematurely his career as a novelist.

A more persistent rebel was George Moore. He tells us in his *Confessions of a Young Man* how he went to Paris at the time when the literary cafés were boiling with discussion of the naturalistic creed of Zola, Maupassant and the Goncourts, and returned to write imitations of them in English. In *A Modern Lover* (now called *Lewis Seymour and Some Women*) he wrote a novel, like Maupassant's *Bel-Ami,* in which promiscuity in sexual relations, guided by an eye to the main chance, is the substance of the story. Moore's masterpiece in fiction is *Esther Waters,* in which a servant girl finds the footman too attractive, and experiences the cruelty of society to the unmarried mother, before William turns up again. Moore is chiefly distinguished for his autobiographical writing which is rich in sexual reminiscence. In *Memoirs of My Dead Life* there is a charmingly frank narrative of a love episode, the "Lovers of Orelay," which in delicacy of treatment does not fall below the great romantic love stories.

A third type of rebel in the last decade of the 19th century was Grant Allen, writer of popular science, whose novel, *The Woman Who Did,* is a belligerent piece of propaganda against marriage as an institution. The heroine holds that the marriage contract is degrading to woman, in granting exclusive rights to her person to a man. It is with the purpose of bringing woman up to a level with man's freedom that the heroine persuades her lover to live with her in free union. His death and the birth of her child bring her face to face with the hostile world, a struggle which she survives until her daughter repudiates her, and prefers marriage bondage to freedom.

Like Grant Allen, Bernard Shaw approached social problems with something of a scientific background. His plays must be accounted among the most awakening influences of recent literature. *Mrs. Warren's Profession,* in the series of *Unpleasant Plays,* treats frankly the subject of prostitution. In *Man and Superman* he puts forth the theory, which he had already expounded in *The Unsocial Socialist,* that woman, as nature's agent for the survival of the race, is the pursuer and man the hunted quarry—an idea which Thackeray had made the subject of his elegant persiflage. In *Getting Married* Shaw deals with the problem of marriage from the point of view of improving the breed of men by scientific mating, as we have done with horses, dogs and cattle. Shaw followed Ibsen in making the stage a vehicle for ideas, and to their joint influence must be attributed the increased realism and seriousness of the English drama to which tendency Pinero, Jones, Maugham, Barker, Galsworthy, to mention but a few recent dramatists, bear witness.

In the Edwardian period, then, the sexual life was presented in literature with a frankness, sincerity, and knowledge forbidden to the Victorian. It is true, the attention of many of the foremost writers—Wells, Galsworthy, Bennett—was given chiefly to post-marital conditions and problems, but two may be mentioned as of special bearing on our theme. D. H. Lawrence made his first great success as a novelist with *Sons and Lovers.* Here the hero, Paul Morel, has two consummated love affairs, one with a girl, one with a married woman, both of which are aborted by the persistence of the tie between Paul and his mother—the Œdipus complex. In *The Rainbow,* Lawrence explores the first love of Ursula Brangwen. In its sequel, *Women in Love,* he traces a double labyrinth of the passions of Ursula and her sister Gudrun, with a morbid emphasis on the sexual act which anticipates *Lady Chatterley's Lover.* In *The Lost Girl* he develops the modern discovery of incongruity, rather than Victorian consistency, as a basis of character. The heroine, brought up in a respectable middle-class family, left an orphan, joins a troop of itinerant performers, falls in love with one of them, and accompanies him to his native village in the mountains of the Abruzzi.

Lawrence in his clinical studies of the love life of the young adult makes much use of the psychoanalytic technique and terminology. In this respect his chief rival is Miss May Sinclair. One of Miss Sinclair's earlier books, *The Combined Maze,* is a study of the sexual tension between two young people whose marriage is delayed by poverty. *The Three Sisters* followed her study of the Brontës, and reproduces in some respects the situation of that lonely family. Of the three sisters, daughters of the rector, one marries out of her class, a farmer. The others are rivals for the only possible male in the vicinity—a young doctor, who falls to the weaker, the less fit of the two, defeating the law of survival. One theme recurs repeatedly in Miss Sinclair's novels, that of frustration of the younger generation by the older. In *The Three Sisters,* the cause is the father. In *The Tree of Heaven,* in *Mary Olivier,* in *Arnold Water-*

*low,* it is the mother whose possessive affection deflects the natural course of young lives. *Mary Olivier* is the most penetrating of these in its representation of vague and evanescent states of consciousness, obscurely related to suppressed sexual impulses. Only too late does Mary give herself to a lover. Miss Sinclair sees the tyranny of family supported by religious scruples. It may be said that she, following Samuel Butler in *The Way of All Flesh,* makes her chief crusade against the three Victorian idols—mother, home, and heaven.

The difference noted in the period after 1890 may be described as literature catching up with life, as fiction under the impulse of science and realism, attempting to record faithfully in all fields what actually happens. Life, of course, was subject to a correlative influence of literature through its diffusion of knowledge of the greater freedom in sexual relations which was coming about with accelerated speed on account of changes in the social structure. Economic conditions, which delayed the financial independence of the male, prolonged premarital engagements with increasing tendency to what the Victorians called incontinence. The so-called emancipation of women, leading to their economic independence, made them more and more independent of marriage, and disposed them to demand the same freedom which men enjoyed in making and breaking tentative sexual arrangements. The higher education of women tended in the same direction. These influences are set forth in Mr. H. G. Wells' *Ann Veronica* (1909). The wide use of the automobile, promoting freedom of movement and releasing individuals from the espionage and criticism of a fixed social group, was another development in relaxing the bonds of good behavior. The decline in authority of the church, the school and the family, as well as of the community, removed barriers in the way of normal, if illicit, indulgence by young people. The diffusion of knowledge of contraceptives and of prophylactic preventives against infection among the cultivated classes made for further license. In short, the restraining influence so aptly noted by a Victorian poet—

> There was a young lady quite wild
> Who kept herself pure, undefiled,
> By thinking of Jesus,
> Venereal diseases
> And the danger of having a child—

became obsolete. That staunch Victorian, G. Lowes Dickinson, wrote: "As I observe from the outside the ways of the modern young, it sometimes seems to me that they are losing everything in a kind of tomcat copulation of the most miscellaneous kind."

These forces operating in the early years of the century were surpassed by the impact of the Great War. On the one hand the imminence of death for a great proportion of young unmarried men led to a demand for a taste of the sweets of life which refused to be denied. This became the theme of innumerable novels, of which Galsworthy's *Saint's Progress* may be cited as a dignified example. On the other hand, the emancipation of men and women from social restraint by virtue of transplantation resulted in an increase of casual promiscuity. This was especially true in the case of the United States, where the government, faring the evil of French prostitution, shipped a great number of presumably well-bred girls to Europe in connection with the Red Cross, canteen or Christian services, where, according to the evidence of literature (*vide* John Dos Passos' *1919,* Mary A. Lee's *It's a Great War,* etc.), some of them certainly did their bit in an unanticipated manner.

All these influences account for the enormous difference between the Victorian novel and that of the present day: whereas in the former the consummation of the sexual relation, whether sanctified by marriage or not, was an event of supreme importance, a crisis or a dénouement in the lives of the participants, today it is coming more and more to be regarded as a commonplace. It is true, tragic implications in premarital intercourse still determine the plots of old-fashioned novels, like Dreiser's *An American Tragedy;* and the possibility of romantic beauty in such relations is not excluded, as in Miss May Sinclair's *Ann Severn and the Fieldings.* The process of seduction is still of high interest, corresponding in this respect to courtship among the Victorians, as is shown by the great though temporary popularity of such books as Miss Frances Newman's *The Hard Boiled Virgin* and Miss Viña Delmar's *Bad Girl.* There is undoubtedly, however, a growing tendency to treat sex relations lightly and casually, as in Miss Rose Macauley's *Dangerous Age* and *Told by an Idiot.* Promiscuity is coming to be an accepted convention in modern fiction as monogamy was in Victorian. An extreme illustration is found in Aldous Huxley's Utopia, *Brave New World,* in which the coming heirs of a mechanized civilization regard sexual intercourse among all and sundry as a function to be determined only by such selective process as governs the choice of food from a varied and appetizing menu. There is certainly something in this tendency to justify Mr. Krutch's forebodings in *The Modern Temper* that literature has thereby been deprived of one of its chief values.

But when the consequences of love were made less momentous, then love itself became less momentous too, and we discovered that the now-lifted veil of mystery was that which made it potentially important as well as potentially terrible. Sex, we learned, was not so awesome as once we had thought; God does not care so much about it as we had formerly been led to suppose; but neither, as a result, do we. Love is becoming gradually so accessible, so unmysterious, and so free that its value is trivial.

It is interesting to note some of the ways in which modern writers are seeking to prevent or delay the loss of this value from their resources. Undoubtedly there is still a large reading public which is sexually naïve, which finds its experience in pulp fiction or moving pictures rather than in life, and for which the mere fact of extra-marital relations affords sufficient excitement. Mrs. Eleanor Glyn's *Three Weeks* is still a standard work. For a more sophisticated audience, however, something new must be provided. The first recourse is naturally to an intensification of the realistic method, of which *The Young Manhood of Studs Lonigan*, by James T. Farrell, is the latest and most powerful example. Here we have the life of a young man narrated with a fullness that would have satisfied Thackeray. The deteriorating influence of the gang, as opposed to that of the family and church, Studs' habitual state of mind in regard to girls of the neighborhood, his feeling for Lucy, which at times approaches love, but which nearly ends in seduction in spite of Studs' infectious disease, his final degradation into a bum of the type familiar to him—this is narrated with a convincing realism which makes the book a social document of high value.

Another method of intensification of the sexual interest is that of explicit detail, of which Frank Harris in his *Autobiography*, and Lawrence in *Lady Chatterley's Lover*, have given conspicuous examples. A third method, also illustrated by Lawrence, is that of bringing science (or some will say pseudo-science) to the reënforcement of realism. An extension of the realistic method into fields hitherto forbidden by good taste is seen in Brieux' play translated by Shaw as *Damaged Goods*, dealing with syphilis, in W. L. George's *A Bed of Roses*, dealing with prostitution. To the need of reviving a flagging interest in sex may be attributed the appearance of novels and plays on the theme of perversion. Sometimes this theme supplies the motive for a genuinely tragic situation, as in Bourdet's play, *The Captive;* sometimes for a serious character study of a Lesbian, as in Miss Radclyffe Hall's *The Well of Loneliness;* sometimes it appears only as a flavoring of human relations as in Rosamund Lehman's *Dusty Answer*, Naomi Royde-Smith's *The Tortoise Shell Cat*, or Elizabeth Bowen's *The Hotel*. Sometimes it is treated with realistic farce as in Compton Mackenzie's *Extraordinary Women*. To the same tendency to find a new motive in sex may perhaps be attributed in part this writer's trilogy of religious experience—*The Altar Steps, The Parson's Progress, The Heavenly Ladder*, a sublimation which George Moore had treated in *Evelyn Innes* and *Sister Teresa*.

These phenomena and tendencies are too near to us in time to be estimated with any approach to accuracy in regard to their bearing on the theme of the love life of the unmarried adult in the literature of the future. It may be that Mr. Wells is right in *The World of William Clissold* in holding that there is far more significant material for fiction than mating. Certainly in a collectivist society, toward which we seem to be moving, such individual proclivities will command less attention and will seem to be of less importance than in the past. If, following Mr. Shaw's advice, the state undertakes seriously to improve the human breed by stud farm methods, the coupling of young men and women will have no more interest than that of bulls and cows. One suspects that the emphasis on sexual relations in *Brave New World* is introduced from the point of view of Mr. Huxley's present readers rather than from that of the inhabitants of Utopia. If it is true that romantic love, that passion peculiar to the unmarried adult, is destined to decline further, and ultimately to fade out as a literary motive, there will be some of us Victorians who will feel the force of Mr. Krutch's elegiac warning: "Every time a value is born, existence takes on a new meaning; every time one dies, some part of that meaning passes away."

# CONDITIONS TODAY

. . . it may be said of all freer forms that there is no way in which to guarantee the happiness of either party save in reliance on the character of the other. This is a most uncertain guarantee.—WILLIAM SUMNER

## SOME MODERN PORTRAITS AND THEIR INTERPRETATION

*Lorine Pruette*
CONSULTING PSYCHOLOGIST

### MODERN PORTRAITS

A LITTLE GROUP of men and women are drinking cocktails in the late afternoon, not very strong cocktails, just enough to lift a little the fatigue that descends upon brain workers when the day is running out. A spinsterish, not very attractive woman of a certain age walks over to a strange man to whom she has not spoken before, and asks him to come out into the hall with her. She faces him quietly, speaking in low tones so that they will not be heard: "I have had twelve men and none of them was any good. I've chosen you for the next one." She waits for him to speak; she thinks that this is a good approach to a man; but there is a kind of despair in her eyes.

A man and a woman are having what purports to be a business conference. "Could you," asks the man, "just speaking hypothetically, or even academically, could you have an affair with me?" The girl is nineteen. She smiles: "I could, but I wouldn't. It would be a bad idea for me to have an affair with a man in this city, for it would get around."

The young man in his early twenties is dark and nervous. "I've had more than twenty women in the last few years" (he is a little desperate) "and only one or two were any good. The best one was a prostitute."

At the conference, the annual conference of this and that, most of the participants stay at the same hotel. Two women make their plans together; by accident a group seems to gather in the room of one of the women and by accident disperse. "Don't go," the woman whispers to one of the men. She sits on the bed and looks at him; the silence gathers about them; he wants to escape; he does not know how to go; he knows what she has been wanting from him all these years during which they have been working together; he is painfully embarrassed for the woman; he kisses her suddenly, ruefully, apologetically—and flees.

The strange young man brings the young girl home and, when he finds that she is alone in the apartment, he suggests that he spend the night with her. "I wouldn't even let him kiss me" (the girl tells the story) "because I liked him so much and because I wanted him to respect me. If I hadn't cared anything about him I would have let him kiss me because I wouldn't have cared whether he respected me or not."

"Of course it would be better to be married," declares the ascetic-looking scholarly man in his early thirties, "more normal, I mean. I resent having to spend so much time on sex—two days and nights a week on a purely sexual association with a woman. I resent it. But I could not bear to be married and live in a small apartment, with no privacy, no escape ever from each other, and I see no way of getting enough money to live any other way."

The young woman wants to get married, but the young man is fearful. So she seduces him, in order to settle the issue, she thinks, but the young man runs away.

The young woman wants her lover to marry her, but he is afraid to divorce his wife, afraid she could not survive this disaster. The girl is not afraid to gamble; she has an illegitimate baby. The older woman agrees to the divorce; the man marries the girl; they are crazy about the baby; they are very happy.

"But what about my sex life?" the woman asks seriously, having recently parted from her lover. "Won't I be unhealthy if I don't find someone else?" And then, as the conversation continues, she asks, "But what is love? I've been infatuated with a number of men, but I never felt this great rushing-out of emotion that one reads about. Perhaps I'm just selfish, or perhaps the stories make you think there is more to sex than there really is."

"Well, see here," asks the young man, "I've had lots of girls but will you kindly tell me what is meant by the spiritual value of love? I've certainly never met anything like that. Do you think I've been missing something? Perhaps our whole hard-boiled generation has been missing something. Do you suppose it is partly the words we use and the rough sort of attitude we take toward the girls? Maybe it would be different if we changed the trimmings, talked like our fathers."

A girl of seventeen is driving down a dark road with a man of twenty-five, the visiting young man whom she, at the moment, passionately adores. The man stops the car, switches off the lights. "Get out," he commands. Suddenly they are fighting, violently, with no quarter asked or given. The girl manages to get into the driver's seat and turns on the engine. The man slumps in the other seat, exhausted. "You'll have to drive," he says, "I can't."

The woman wants the man to marry her. She reminds him that she was a virgin when he took her. He coarsely assures her that she has not been damaged, that, in fact, she is improved, so what is she crying about? He breaks with her brutally; he is afraid she will trap him.

A man and a woman have been living together for some time, when the man begins to insist on marriage. The woman is eager to go on with her work and thinks that marriage will make life more difficult. He insists that she will be as free afterward, as before; she is afraid, but she takes the risk; she finds that the husband demands much more than the lover.

"We belong to the generation," says a girl of twenty-five, "that has to have some belief in romantic love, even though we know that it is a bourgeois concept that is passing. But, even so, we know that a woman is much better off not to marry a man, if she hopes to do anything more than be married." The girl has been living for several years with a man to whom she is not married; she is housekeeper, assistant, all that a wife might be expected to be, but she feels that her position is safer than it would be if the man fell into the habit of thinking of her as his wife.

"After I passed thirty, I stopped counting them," says a young woman in discussing her lovers. "But at any rate I know this, that I have no more curiosity about men and that I can never feel cheated, the way so many married women feel. They keep wondering if they have missed something, and wanting a little fling. Well, I've had mine." Now she is happily married.

These true vignettes, drawn from different parts of the country, might be multiplied indefinitely. It is a bold individual, even an incautious one, who would dare to generalize with any great assurance on the subject of the sex life of the unmarried today. Statistical studies are few and limited; case histories drawn from the records of psychiatrists and psychologists are always somewhat suspect, as not being illustrative of the lives of those who do not find it necessary to seek such assistance. Stories and novels, while growing inevitably out of the social milieu, and conditioned inevitably by the personal experience of the writers, are subject to much the same criticism as the case histories of the specialists. Newspaper stories are obviously selected for their novel aspects, rather than for their representation of the average behavior of large masses of people. Our personal experiences, of course, are also definitely selective, so that one person with complete honesty of purpose—conscious honesty, let us say—will observe certain trends, while another will observe other trends. Thus any generalizations which appear in this chapter must be accepted as the tentative conclusions of an individual who freely acknowledges that she may be wrong, but does not, of course, really think she is.

Probably there will be no disputing the obvious fact that we no longer protect the virginity of our girls in the stricter fashion of many other ages. The disappearance of the chaperon, the mobility provided by the automobile and the aeroplane, the sexual stimulation of the motion picture, the greater freedom for experimentation possible to the working girl or woman as contrasted with that of the stay-at-home girl, the greater ease of association between the sexes in smoking, drinking, golfing or in the following of other sports—all these factors make it more likely that the woman will be exposed to a variety of sexual stimulations and that she will not have the obvious protections once provided by a stricter society. To be sure, we shall never know how much sexual experimentation really existed in past years within the closer confines of the family circle, but at least we can say that today the mathematical probability of sex experience is greatly increased. We can also say that a great many girls are today being sexually aroused at a much earlier age than was true of their older sisters and mothers. The sexual strains and tensions of the adolescent boy have been abundantly recognized; it would appear that today we must at least suspect an approximation of the adolescent girl's experience to that of the adolescent boy. This raises the enormously interesting question of whether the young girl is physiologically and psychologically as well adapted to endure the experience of sexual excitation and frustration as is the young boy. It is my own belief that she is not.

Various factors are being suggested to explain the great initiative of the modern woman in seeking sexual experience, or at least in seeking with greater determination and directness the company of men. This earlier and more frequent excitation of the young girl should not be ignored in the list of such factors. Gone are the days when the young woman was content to wait in dreamy solitude, busy with her hope chest and her hopes, for the young Lochinvar from out of the West. She has learned that she too can bestride a horse and go seeking for what she desires and go she does.

This fact makes for both amusing and tragic complications. In many cases it is perfectly clear that the young boy is not displeased by having the girls assume much of the initiative of the courtship phase. Older men and women will very commonly retort that this is not the way for a girl "to get a man," but old saws are not necessarily true merely because they are old. In many cases the evidence shows that this is exactly how a girl does so, by deliberately going after him. Women are trained to far greater social initiative and responsibility than men, and sexual experience is a part of social life. The only time that men take a social initiative is under this driving spur of need for sexual satisfaction; there is no obvious reason why they would not in a great many cases be glad to surrender this initiative also to the activities of women.

Nevertheless, the traditionalists have a certain wisdom on their side. In the present confused state of our sexual mores, to call out her horse and go roaming the world in search of her man carries very real dangers for the girl. She must unquestionably expect to be hurt much more often than in the passive stage. She cannot take over the right to propose herself to the young man without ceding him the right to refuse her, or later to jilt her. Freedom is always a two-edged sword; the younger generations of women appear able to wield this without doing themselves irreparable damage; in many cases older women do not. Two of the happiest young women of my acquaintance are girls who only a few months ago were cruelly, bitterly, tragically jilted by the men to whom they had "given themselves." One girl is married to another man, the other has a job and many other boys to afford her diversions. They have both come through a difficult experience with flying colors, but we must not forget that they have had a period of very genuine suffering. Had they been ten or fifteen years older it is quite possible that they would have developed some very undesirable neurotic traits.

Older women—and older men—cannot throw off all of their early heritage, so that when their egos are deflated and they are torn by personal loss and frustration the woman reverts to the apparent protections of the code she learned in childhood, calls the man who has hurt her "a cad," discovers unexpected ideals about love, the family, fidelity, and so on, to which when happy she had not subscribed. In the same way the man who is growing a little weary of an affair, or who is growing fearful that this may progress into too close a relation, may revert to the traditions of his childhood. Those traditions assert unequivocally that "men don't marry women like that," in spite of the fact that men always did to some degree—and recently to a considerable degree. Nevertheless, men, seeking a way out for themselves, not infrequently act similarly to the hurt woman with her talk of "cads"; childish ideas of pollution and immorality are brought out of their recesses and given a new coating, and the man discovers that he actually shrinks from the woman to whom a little while before he was vowing eternal devotion.

Thus the double standard continues to flourish, in spite of the fact that this term is no longer fashionable. The double standard is simply a protective device used by both men and women to proclaim that what is sauce for the goose is not sauce for the gander, or vice versa. In each case it is used to claim special privilege for the sex of the person using it. It is only the rare person who continues to revise his beliefs and attitudes as he grows older. Most of us try to cling to them all; what we learned from our parents, what we learned in school, what we read and like in books, what our present social group approves. Thus in time of crisis we have a variety of attitudes to choose from and inevitably we reach for the attitude which frees us most easily, which protects our ego and seemingly justifies whatever we do. It is because of this storehouse of conflicting views, which most of us keep with us, that men and women who have been lovers can be so extraordinarily cruel to each other.

Exploitation of a man by a woman, of a woman by a man, is a commonplace of the present day, among the married as well as the unmarried. Fear, trickery and uncertain approaches, a denial of responsibility for their own deeds, a flight from painful reality, these also are commonplaces in countless stories of unmarried lovers. These complications are not new; the new aspect is contributed by the numbers experiencing them today. It has been a long, slow process to tame the anarchism and egotism of the sexual drive in men or women; now that so many of the customary safeguards and standards are in question it is not surprising that the sex life of the unmarried adult of today presents such a dark, stormy, and unesthetic picture.

The common "necking" party is a folkway of the present age. It is participated in by countless persons of all ages who suffer genuine feelings of shame and loss afterwards. The mores, abstract formalized conceptions based on past experience, are obviously slower to change than the folkways. The girl who gladly goes in for "necking," and then fears that she has lost the boy's respect, the boy who persuades his fiancée into a sexual relation and then rejects her as not fit to be the mother of his children, are both illustrating the cultural lag in adjustment between the mores and the folkways of sexual behavior. The girls who band together to make life unhappy for the boy who is guilty of such a dishonest trick are doing their part in the development of new mores of responsibility for both sexes. Nevertheless, the very wide gulf between the sexual mores and folkways of today accounts for much youthful cynicism and maturer bitterness, a *faute-de-mieux* approach to an unintegrated situation.

Once there were relatively fixed patterns of sexual behavior into which people fitted themselves according to age, sex and social and financial status. The rôles were assigned by something outside the individual and there were fewer problems of individual choice. Even when the individual did not always fulfill his rôle he had the comfort of knowing that it existed, as something toward which he would some day progress. Many today are uncertain about their standards of morality in other fields as well as in sex, but nowhere does more pain and trouble seem to follow than in this field. It is possible that the sexual experimentation of the unmarried today may give way to another phase of inhibitions and restrictions; if so, it will have contributed nothing new to the history of the race. On the other hand, there is at least the possibility that new and far more adult standards of behavior are now being slowly evolved. Our business ethics today are surely in a dubious state, but if sexual ethics could advance to the level of honesty and responsibility now to be found in business this would be a very genuine advance. In sexual behavior almost every one remains the complete child, greedy, egoistic, anarchistic, cowardly. This has been largely because this aspect of life has been hidden from exposure, has been protected from the powerful influence of social criticism. The gulf between folkway and mores, between action and belief, should be bridged by knowledge and frankness among men and women and between the various generations. Exploitation is common enough in the industrial world but even more common in sexual relations; denial of responsibility for one's actions is still sadly common in both.

Important social changes which affect the present picture will occur to all of us. Among them must be mentioned the socially approved use of alcoholic liquors in circles which before the "noble experiment" had not so indulged. This is particularly important for young people who do not yet know how to carry their liquor or their sex. Few sights are more offensive than that of a roomful of college boys and girls half asleep from liquor, half wild from sexual excitement, alternating between stimulating dancing and draping themselves about each other in corners, necking and dozing and fumbling with each other. The use of the automobile develops the picture one step further, in a direction easily understood.

Another change of importance is the dissemination of birth control information. This has a double effect, cutting down the fear of impregnation when contraceptive devices are used and also when they are not. The old idea that one false step meant an illegitimate child has been discarded, both by the young people who use contraceptive methods and by those who take a chance. The possibility of an actual decline in fertility is suggested by the large number who find the latter process relatively safe. On the other hand, many have developed techniques of mutual stimulation which do not carry the danger of impregnation but which raise serious questions as to their effect upon a later conventional marriage adjustment.

The realism of the U.S.S.R. in making abortion legal is a challenge to the decency of other countries which allow this service to be exploited in a dangerous and unregulated manner, threatening the health and lives of countless young women each year, as well as endangering their later potential motherhood. However, there are evidences that enlightened members of the medical profession in this country are working for a saner and more humane approach to the problem, in spite of the powerful opposition of certain groups. It should be clear that it is the young, the ignorant and the frightened who are in greatest danger from the abortion racket. It is also clear that an increasing number of idealistic and responsible physicians are performing such operations, and that the only way of protecting the health of our young women is by bringing this whole matter out into the open where it can be supervised by responsible professional organizations. Some young people discover that an abortion is not such a dangerous affair as once they thought and develop a carelessness about it quite in line with their carelessness about contraception. The fact is that a little knowledge gives them a false feeling of security and that they quite fail to realize its serious hazards.

A further social change of great importance is the breakdown of the patriarchal family. This is especially pertinent to our subject, as it results in unmarried women living away from home, earning their own living and responsible to no one but themselves for their behavior. In a recent novel a mother is quoted as telling her daughter that she may do what she likes in sexual matters because economically she is a boy. Once we should have referred to this situation as the economic independence of women but today we are wary of using the term economic independence for anyone.

Indeed, a recent aspect may be expressed as a growing feeling of economic insecurity on the part of both men and women. Just as sexual license may be an accompaniment of war, it may also be an accompaniment of the critical times of the depression through which the world has recently been passing. Economic insecurity may foster a feeling of recklessness, of taking what pleasures are to be secured in a most unsatisfactory world. It may also foster in both men and women an increased desire for marriage, as a possible refuge in an uncertain existence, while at the same time increasing the difficulties of setting up a satisfactory marriage. One young woman, when reminded that there was little reason to expect that a man would necessarily be able to support her or to provide her with more security than she had in herself, answered succinctly, "Well, there would be two chances instead of one." A further effect of economic insecurity sometimes shows itself in men, driving them to seek in the conquest of women a reassurance as to their capacity to dominate in some situation. The full story of the effect of the depression upon the folkways of sex cannot yet be told—because we do not know it. The effects of despair, of feeling detached and unplaced in a changing world, will be, we are compelled to hope, merely temporary; but the effects of increased leisure and of increased mechanization of life, both of which may very possibly enhance sexual activity, we should expect to be permanently with us.

The declining control of the church is still another social change affecting sexual behavior. One girl reports that the only virgins she knows are the girls who are very religious but, she adds, she doesn't know many virgins.

The unmarried adult has a limited number of possibilities before him. It is evidence of a considerable change in popular thinking that a book with the title of the present volume could be produced. Until now it has been the custom for society in this country to avert its eyes from the subject of the sex life of unmarried males and stoutly to deny that such a thing existed for unmarried females. We must not forget that only a few decades ago no lady or good woman, even though married, was thought to have a sex life. Now, at least in certain circles, popular thinking has swung to the other extreme and women compelled to endure a temporary period of continence claim to be gravely concerned about the wholesomeness of their lives; while it is not at all uncommon for men of liberal tendencies to condemn the entire army of school teachers on the ground that they are virgins and hence incompetent to teach. Thus the views of mankind swing perpetually back and forth on this absorbing subject of sex.

The adjustments possible for the unmarried may be summed up under the following headings: chastity, masturbation, homosexuality, heterosexuality (including the butterfly, the week-ender and the progressive monogamist). Of these, none has been subject to greater misconception than has chastity. The story writers are seldom able to interpret this as anything but a negative and undesirable state; it is therefore particularly interesting to find D. H. Lawrence, in *Lady Chatterley's Lover*, speaking vigorously in praise of chastity. At the close of the book, when the lovers are to be separated for a number of months, Mellors writes to Connie: "I love being chaste now. . . . Now is the time to be chaste, it is so good to be chaste, like a river of cool water in my soul. I love the chastity now that it flows between us. It is like fresh water and rain. How can men want wearisomely to philander. What a misery to be like Don Juan, and impotent ever to——oneself into peace, and the little flame alight, impotent and unable to be chaste in the cool between-whiles, as by a river."

Many persons who consider themselves modern and realistic seem actually to fear a period of being without sexual expression. They walk on a treadmill of sex, on principle, as it were, rather than because of desire—little Don Juans, perpetually seeking reassurance as to their sexual capacities. The notion that men can be chaste is particularly offensive to many women. I once made myself extremely unpopular with a class of red-lipped maidens by assuring them that it was quite possible for men to view them without an immediate and perpetual stirring of desire; the young women shook their heads at me sadly, declining to surrender one jot or tittle of their cherished belief in their unending danger from the carnality of the male. Since the rise of psychoanalysis, it is becoming more and more common to question the adaptability of the unmarried and presumably virgin woman for a variety of jobs, particularly for school teaching. This is rather absurd, for there is no evidence whatever that married women have less sexual conflict than those who are living without any overt sexual expression, while there is some evidence to suggest that married women suffer more than their virginal sisters from the burden of sexual discontent and dissatisfaction. If we lay aside our theories and look at the people about us it becomes clear that individual differences must be allowed to play their important rôle in this as in other relations and that while some men and women appear incapable of living without sexual expression, others have no difficulty in so doing.

Actually, there is very little respect anywhere for chastity. The philosophy of even the most conservative groups esteems this as something compulsory, like a jail sentence, from which men and women will escape by any means in their power. This is an unfortunate approach, for periods must come in the lives of all which make chastity imperative or at least desirable. The American concept of romantic love requires a concept of voluntary chastity, but it seems far more probable that the Russians will in their greater freedom of sexual expression arrive at a respect for chastity as a matter of choice. Perhaps our own experimental youth may eventually develop this conception—perhaps—but not tomorrow.

Then there is the adjustment made through masturbation, over the wisdom of which the authorities continue to quarrel while showing a steady inclination toward greater tolerance. Great numbers of people take this way out, in sorrow or in sickness or when they are unavoidably alone. It seems probable that boys develop this habit earlier than girls, or let us say that more women in their twenties turn for the first time to this release than is true of men. Self-stimulation is an unsocial habit, which may make normal sexual relations more difficult, but its chief danger lies in the sense of guilt and shame which so often accompany the practice.

On the subject of homosexuality the views of society also swing on the pendulum. Not so long ago Berlin's cafés for homosexuals and Lesbians were well-known and famous; the Nazis closed them for obvious reasons. The average American is particularly embittered on this topic, and he likes it no better when he learns of the Greek view of love between men. The experimental homosexuals are not important, but the permanent homosexuals are an unfortunate and exploited group. They show all the psychology of any underprivileged group and develop theories that turn their behavior into the expression of a cult. They search history and literature for the evidence that great men and women were in love with their own sex; they strive to prove that this adjustment of the sexual life is the only one possible, determined for them by biology. They do not, of course, accept the view that they represent a state of arrested development, remaining perpetually at a stage through which most, if not all, boys and girls pass at an early age.

Society is customarily very unkind to these unfortunate persons. In the attempt to escape from a sense of abnormality, a considerable number undertake marriage, sometimes on the advice of physicians, and this leads to disaster in various ways. Homosexual relations cut the individual off from the main current of social life and subject him to all the undesirable developments which appear in any group which feels itself discriminated against and maltreated. Where a definite cult develops, with delusions of superiority to the vulgar, "normal" mob, proselyting tendencies are also likely to appear, which in part explains society's repugnance to such groups. However, the aversion of the average person to the entire subject seems sufficiently exaggerated to remind us of the Freudian dictum as to the relation between fear and desire. If we do not accept the theory of biological inevitability, it would seem that society's best defense against such groups lies not in hounding or oppressing the individual homosexual, but in seeking to develop more satisfactory sexual relations between men and women and more wholesome family life from which the children will gain their own norms of behavior.

Some unmarried adults inaugurate sexual relations with members of the opposite sex but find themselves unable to maintain any valid relation over a period of time. These we may call the butterflies. They appear to be afflicted with defective vision, so that they are unable to perceive the charms of the flower from which they have just sipped but must forever be winging their way in quest of more distant delights. If they meet their own kind, such persons do little damage, but very often this is not the case. The wandering butterfly is himself forever uncertain, always seeking to believe that this time it will endure, that here at last is found the haven of permanence. Young people without economic independence are often forced by circumstances into the rôle of the butterfly, and they may acquire such habits of shifting from sexual partner to sexual partner as to make an enduring fixation upon one person almost impossible. Most of the dicta about love have been built up on the behavior of the butterfly—married as well as unmarried—and in recent years the poetry of Edna St. Vincent Millay, Dorothy Parker and others has been hailed with delight because it expressed the philosophy of the butterfly when confronted with love.

But, just as there is in human beings the continued thirst for new experience, so is there also the continued desire for security, permanence and continuity of living. It is indeed possible to argue that there is only one type of experience possible to a given individual, and the published memoirs of some of the most determined butterflies show a monotonous similarity in their various episodes, as when Frank Harris writes at length about women and all his women seem to be of the same pattern. Circumstances, convenience, economics and other factors lead a great many out of the flitting class into the week-enders. For these, the relationship may take on a certain stability, except when interrupted by external circumstances. One man now among the week-ending group reports that he spends about three days a week with a woman who interests him solely as a sexual object, and that while he cannot escape from this preoccupation with sex, nevertheless he resents having to spend so much of his time in this way.

A more continuous relationship is set up by those who may be called the progressive monogamists. Here a man and a woman may live in the same place and set up a domestic establishment which satisfies their desires for love and stability for the time being, just as marriage would, but which leaves the way open for escape when the relationship palls. There is no great difference between these individuals and the married couples who turn to divorce with growing frequency. Indeed, some of the unmarried who live in this monogamous relationship seem to find it more difficult to break with the illegal partner than do those who are married. A considerable number of independent and intellectual young women definitely prefer the arrangement of progressive monogamy to that of marriage, holding that they thus escape the burdens of the conventional masculine attitude toward the wife and retain a genuine advantage by the appearance of giving from desire rather than from legal fiat. In many cases the unconventional domestic arrangement leads to legal marriage. Young women who have gone through this process report that the husband's vocabulary often suffers an amazing change, and that phrases such as, "I won't permit you," suddenly appear in the family discussions. The wife also mysteriously changes, in some cases, and begins to seek the use of the ancient prerogatives of wifely claims. Judge Lindsay reports the amusing story of a young couple who lived together quite happily until they were married, found it impossible to get along as soon as they had received the legal sanction, but reverted to a happy relationship on being told that they were no longer married. There are many arguments to be made in favor of the conception put forward by John B. Watson that marriage should not be permitted until the man and the woman have lived together for a reasonable period of time, in order to make certain that they are adjusted to each other. On the other hand, a considerable body of experience is accumulating to suggest that adjustment outside matrimony is no necessary guarantee of adjustment within the social, traditional institution of marriage, and that their happiness as lovers may work against, as well as for, happiness as married partners.

It is obvious that the divorced and the widowed, as well as the single, may establish relationships under the butterfly, the week-ender or the progressive monogamy type. It seems probable that the divorced are less able than the widowed to accept a life without sexual relationships, particularly in the early days after the divorce when the individual not infrequently takes refuge in promiscuity as he might take to drugs. Nobody has adequately discussed the joys of widowhood, and the change often experienced by widows who emerge from a mousey, repressed wifehood to take on many of the more vivid and dominant characteristics of the husband. Why this should be so is a subject for interesting speculation. Frances Newman appears to have answered it to her own satisfaction, if not to ours, by the title of her novel, *Dead Lovers Are Faithful Lovers*, but it is obvious that much more than this is involved. I have not observed any analogous change in widowers, who seem often to become more dependent upon women than ever before.

A great part of adult life is shaped and colored by the sexual desires, whether these are indulged or resisted. Even so strong a drive as the sexual shows itself capable of considerable adaptability, of finding satisfactions in a variety of ways. It is not possible to judge any of these ways by theory alone; the test lies in the practice, and it must be pragmatic. Does the relationship tend to produce a well-integrated, competent and desirable member of society? Applied to specific individuals, such a question finds a possible justification for any adjustment, given certain conditioning circumstances. Nevertheless, the unmarried as well as the married appear to accept the condition of legal matrimony as the most desirable. Americans are a much-married people and the prevalence of divorce indicates not only certain unpleasant aspects of human nature but, also, a genuine reaching out toward an ideal which has not yet been realized. Marriage is the goal of almost everyone at some time. In spite of the fact that modern marriage is a chaotic and often revolting spectacle, it remains the goal toward which most people strive. Why, then, do the unmarried not marry, and why do the married not remain married?

Answers to this question would carry us far beyond the confines of this book but it may be possible to cast a hasty glance, a hasty and very superficial glance, at the concepts of marriage, sex and love as these exist in the thinking of many young unmarried men and women, and to speculate as to what these concepts may presage for the future.

It is evident that in the thinking of post-war generations sex has abundantly come into its own. Whatever else the great amount of sexual experimentation may mean, it must surely mean the disappearance of the conventional concept of the frigid woman, for young women today appear to have a direct and definite desire for sexual experience. This introduction of honesty in place of coquetry should mean a great deal to lovers.

There is however a real danger that the expectations developed outside matrimony will meet with serious disappointments when two young people set up housekeeping together and discover that marriage means far more than sex. Particularly in these days of economic crises which inevitably affect the sex drive is it likely that serious misunderstandings may arise. The boy and the girl have been accustomed to meet under certain difficulties, if not dangers; their desire has had definite obstacles to surmount and so has grown stronger and more overwhelming. With marriage these external obstacles seem to have disappeared. The boy, if he is supporting the girl or assuming the major financial responsibility—as most men still need to do to protect their own egos—turns much of his libido into the economic struggle. If he loses his job, or if financial difficulties become extreme, he may become temporarily impotent. Complications in the girl's life may likewise affect her sexual drive, making it sometimes less and in other cases more. Then what heartaches and misunderstandings may not arise, leading each to conclude that "it is not the same." Quarrels and strain may develop not so much from the absence of adequate sexual release as from the conviction of each that they should be having it. Suspicion may arise, hurt pride may lead to "cheating," sex and finances may become more and more tangled, as cause and effect, so that sometimes a marriage is broken which should have endured. How much impotence has been developed in husbands ridden by financial worry cannot be known. One suspects that many disasters have followed from this or from the difficult situation of the husband's earning less than the wife. If a sexual adjustment had already been made under the more artificial conditions of unmarried life, the misunderstandings may be all the greater now.

Young people today have learned something about sex, although not so much as they think, and they have a love pattern based on their relations to their parents. When they bring this equipment into marriage an endless struggle sometimes begins as to which one shall fill the rôle of child, which that of parent. At present there seems to be a special appeal in marriage, as if it offered the haven of the maternal arms. Yet in this storm-tossed world of today, with wars and revolutions threatening all over the globe, with vast economic changes proceeding rapidly, marriage offers less than its wonted security for the emotionally immature. There probably never has been a time in the history of this country when marriage presented so many difficulties. It seems altogether reasonable to expect the total of broken homes, irregular alliances and divorces to increase greatly during the next few years. Yet, in spite of this, marriage offers very definite advantages for the young, when contrasted with years of hopeless waiting for a mate or with the chaotic conditions of unmarried connections.

Young people today show a definite desire to be married, a definite, perhaps even an exaggerated, appreciation of the importance of sex and definite indication of a reaction against the earlier hardboiled cynical approach to love. For a time there seemed a tendency among the intellectual youth to mock at the reality of love, and such phrases as "biological urge" enjoyed popularity as the complete explanation of relations between men and women. It is particularly significant that a new romanticism shows signs of developing, based not on the Victorian gulf between the sexes but on a very binding acquaintance. If this should continue, a real advance may be made in the development of stable and rewarding marriages.

Humanity has always tended to separate love and sex, or love and marriage. The American tradition took a first step toward centering both appeals in the same object as the basis for romantic marriage. But this earlier form was based on the romance of ignorance and disappeared with great rapidity, often on the honeymoon. To be sure, marriage is a relation which must suffer change with the years, but there seems to be a promise of something new in the determination of sexually experienced youth to find a genuine love relation. Once they realize that the achievement of this in marriage is both rare and difficult, the conception of marriage may be revised to suit a modern world. Even today marriage is generally regarded as something fixed, settled, the answer to a question rather than the raising of other questions. This is a conception belonging to patriarchal society in which the family had economic significance. Now that the major reason for marriage is being translated into a response to affectional needs, it becomes much more important to discover some means of establishing stability on these needs. As the birth-rate continues to decline, the bonds of parenthood will be less effective in holding marriages together and for many couples the only possible reason for continuing to live together will be because they like each other.

However, marriage in the civilized world has not been based on mutual affection, but on mutual advantage. Thus in the future of the young people of today there lies the opportunity to develop a new form of marriage, based on the love of mature men and women. Marriage should lose its aspect of retreat to the nursery and take on the challenge of adventure into the unknown. Enormously complex problems remain to be solved if a true marriage between equals is to be developed, based on nothing more tangible than liking each other. Marriage ceases to be an important economic institution, although it continues to carry social implications of vast importance; its primary significance becomes, however, one of a psychological relationship. The young people of today who are so eager to marry probably do not suspect that they are entering the most difficult and dangerous of all relationships. When they do suspect this, perhaps the adventurous drive of mankind will be turned for the first time toward the institution of matrimony, instead of away from it. If this happens, as it may, then the lives of all should be colored by a new excitement, sustained by a new endeavor.

## QUESTIONS WITHOUT ANSWERS

ARE THE unmarried adults of today healthier by reason of their greater freedom? Are they happier?

Do the altered mores afford the unmarried satisfying compensations for marriage?

Do the greater freedoms in sex relationships yield satisfactions commensurate with anticipations from a new experience?

Are the breaking down of older barriers of modesty and shame, taboos and traditions accompanied by greater peace of mind?

Are the unmarried happier as a result of shifting from Puritanic concepts to hedonistic experimentation?

At what price are the new adjustments of the unmarried secured? What is the cost to the individual and his personality? To social adaptation? To society?

What effects do freer sexual activities have upon basic attitudes toward the family? Children? Social interests?

Are there advantages in sexual freedoms in terms of personal economics? Social welfare?

What have been the results, since the Great War, of the greater extension of sexual rights and privileges assumed in unmarriage?

Is permanent homosexuality increasing?

Is there a freedom from all sense of guilt, shame or sin from transcending what once were absolute codes of behavior for the unmarried?

Are there advantages in personal adjustment to the home that enter into and arise from personal formulae for sexual adjustment?

Is the bachelor maid of today happier than the spinster of yesterday?

Do premarital experimentations conduce to happier marriages?

What changes in sentiments arise as a result of freer sexual experimentation?

What elements of sexual adaptation most influence personal happiness?

Are the unmarried happier than ever before? Are they satisfied with their own sexual adjustments, whether based upon homosexuality or heterosexuality, involving an occasional experience or week-ending, or living and loving, with mutual yielding in a monogamous relationship lacking civil sanction to a vow of fidelity?

Countless other questions will occur to readers. Hints at various answers are scattered throughout the volume, but no book can solve the personal problems of all individuals.

Individual adjustments must be the outgrowth of one's own scheme of personal adaptation. Each unmarried adult who raises a personally centered question must answer it in terms of his own constitution, training, experience, and in the light of his understanding of the meaning and reflexive portent of a dynamic sex life in unmarriage.

IRA S. WILE, M.D.

## REFERENCES FOR ARTICLE BY IRA S. WILE


Bloch, Iwan, *The Sexual Life of Our Time.* New York: Allied Book Co., 1925.

Buckle, Henry, T., *History of Civilization in England.* London: Longmans, Green Co., 1873.

Calverton, V. F., and Schmalhausen, Samuel, (Ed.), *Sex in Civilization.* New York: The Macaulay Co., 1929.

Davis, Katharine Bement, *Factors in the Sex Life of 2200 Women.* New York: Harper & Brothers, 1929.

DeTocqueville, Alexis, *Democracy in America.* New York: The Colonial Press, 1900.

Dickinson, Robert Latou, and Beam, Laura, *The Single Woman.* Baltimore: The Williams & Wilkins Co., 1934.

Eddy, Sherwood, *Sex and Youth.* New York: Doubleday Doran & Co., 1928.

Edwards, Alba M., *Marital Condition of Occupied Women.* Reprint, Chap. 5, Vol. 5, "Fifteenth Census Report on Population." Washington, D. C.: Government Printing Office, 1932.

Elliott, Grace L., and Bone, Harry, *The Sex Life of Youth.* New York: Association Press, 1929.

Ellis, Havelock, *Little Essays of Love and Virtue.* London: A. & C. Black, Ltd., 1922.

*The Task of Social Hygiene.* London: Constable and Co., Ltd., 1922.

Galloway, T. W., *Sex and Social Health.* New York: The American Social Hygiene Association, 1924.

Goldberg, B. Z., *The Sacred Fire.* New York: Horace Liveright, Inc., 1930.

Goodsell, Willystine, *A History of the Family as a Social and Educational Institution.* New York: The Macmillan Co., 1930.

Groves, E. R., and Ogburn, W. F., *American Marriage and Family Relationships.* New York: Henry Holt & Co., 1928.

Haire, Norman, *Hymen or the Future of Marriage.* New York: E. P. Dutton & Co., 1928.

Hamilton, G. V., *A Research in Marriage.* New York: Charles & Albert Boni, 1929.

Heisterman, Carl, A., *Memorandum on the Age at which Children*

*Are Permitted to Marry*. Washington, D. C.: Children's Bureau, 1931.

Howard, George Elliot, *A History of Matrimonial Institutions*. Chicago: University of Chicago Press, 1904.

Lea, Henry C., *An Historical Sketch of Sacerdotal Celibacy in the Christian Church*. Boston: Houghton Mifflin Co., 1884.

Letourneau, Charles, *The Evolution of Marriage*. London: Walter Scott, Ltd., 1898.

Malinowski, Bronislaw, *The Sexual Life of Savages*. New York: Horace Liveright, Inc., 1920.

*Sex and Repression in Savage Society*. New York: Harcourt, Brace & Co., 1927.

Margold, Chas. W., *Sex Freedom and Social Control*. Chicago: University of Chicago Press, 1926.

Meagher, John F. W., *A Study of Masturbation and the Psychosexual Life*. New York: William Wood & Co., 1929.

Messer, Mary B., *The Family in the Making*. New York: G. P. Putnam's Sons, 1925.

Sumner, William G., *Folkways*. Boston: Ginn & Co., 1906.

Thwing, Charles F., and Carrie F. B., *The Family*. Boston: Lee & Shepard, 1887.

Wile, Ira S., and Winn, Mary Day, *Marriage in The Modern Manner*. New York: The Century Co., 1929.

Worthington, George, and Topping, Ruth, *Specialized Courts Dealing with Sex Delinquency*. New York: Frederick H. Hitchcock, 1925.

## REFERENCES FOR ARTICLE BY MARGARET MEAD

Aptekar, H. Anjea, *Infanticide, Abortion, Contraception in Primitives*. New York: William Godwin, Inc., 1931.

Briffault, R., *The Mothers*. London: Allen Unwin, 1927; New York: The Macmillan Co., 1927.

Fortune, R. F., *Sorcerers of Dobu*. London: Routledge and Sons, Ltd., 1931; New York: E. P. Dutton & Co., 1932.

"Manus Religion". *Oceania*, September, 1931, pp. 74–108.

Junod, H., *The Story of a South African Tribe*. London: The Macmillan Co., 1927, 2nd edition.

Landtman, G., *The Kiwai Papuans of British New Guinea*. London: The Macmillan Co., 1927.

Loeb, E., "Mentawei Social Organization." *American Anthropologist*.

Berkeley: University of California, n.s. Vol. 30, No. 3, p. 408, July-September, 1928.

Malinowski, B., *The Sexual Life of Savages in Western Melanesia.* London: Routledge and Sons, 1928; New York: Horace Liveright, Inc., 1929.

Mead, Margaret, *Coming of Age in Samoa.* New York: William Morrow & Co., 1928; London: Jonathan Cape, 1929.

*Growing Up in New Guinea.* New York: William Morrow & Co., 1930; London: Routledge & Sons, 1931.

"Adolescence in Primitive and Modern Society" in *The New Generation.* Edited by Samuel B. Schmalhausen and V. F. Calverton. New York: Thomas B. Macaulay Co., 1931.

*The Changing Culture of an Indian Tribe.* New York: Columbia University Press, 1932.

Thurston, E., *Castes and Tribes of Southern India.* Vol. 5. Madras: 1909.

## *General Discussions of Marriage, Sex and the Position of Women in Primitive Society.*

Bachofen, J. J., *Das Mutterrecht.* Stuttgart: Hoffmann, 1861. New York: Boni and Liveright.

Crawley, A. E., *The Mystic Rose.* Edited by Thomas Besterman. London: Methuen, 1927.

Hartland, E. S., *Primitive Society.* New York: E. P. Dutton & Co., 1921.

Lowie, R. H., *Primitive Society.* New York: Boni & Liveright, 1920.

Mead, Margaret, "The Position of Women in Primitive Society." *The Encyclopedia of the Social Sciences.* New York: The Macmillan Co., 1930–1934.

Morgan, L. H., *Ancient Society.* New York: Charles H. Kerr & Co., 1877.

Westermark, E., *The History of Human Marriage.* London: The Macmillan Co., 1901.

## *Discussion of Other Human Traits from the Same Point of View.*

Benedict, R. F., "Culture and the Abnormal." *Journal of General Psychology.* Worcester: 1934, Vol. 10, pp. 59–82.

*Patterns of Culture.* Boston: Houghton Mifflin Co., 1934.

Mead, Margaret, "Jealousy, Primitive and Civilized" in *Woman's Coming of Age*. Edited by S. B. Schmalhausen and V. F. Calverton. New York: Horace Liveright, Inc., 1932.

"An Ethnologist's Footnote to 'Totem and Tabu'." Washington: *The Psychoanalytic Review,* Vol. 17, No. 3, pp. 297-304, July, 1930.

## *Other Recent Publications Which Give Material on the Sexual Life of Primitive People.*

Earthy, Dora B., *Valenga Women.* Published for the International Institute of African Language and Culture, by the Oxford University Press, London: 1933.

Hogbin, H. Ian, "The Sexual Life of the Natives of Ontong Java (Solomon Islands)." *Journal of the Polynesian Society,* Vol. 40, No. 1, March, 1931.

Powdermaker, H., *Life in Lesu,* a Study of a Melanesian Society in New Ireland. New York: W. W. Norton & Co., 1933.

Roheim, G., "Roheim Australasian Research Number" of *The International Journal of Psycho-Analysis.* Vol. 13, Parts 1-2, January-April. London: 1932.

## REFERENCES FOR ARTICLE BY N. W. INGALLS

Davis, Katherine Bement, "Periodicity of Sex Desire." St. Louis: *American Journal of Obstetrics and Gynecology,* Volume 12, December, 1926.

Ellis, Havelock, *Studies in the Psychology of Sex*. Philadelphia: F. A. Davis Co., 1913.

Forel, August, *The Sexual Question.* Rebman Co., 1908.

Marshall, F. H. A., *The Physiology of Reproduction.* New York: Longmans, Green & Co., 1922.

Miller, G. S., Jr., "The Primate Basis of Human Sexual Behavior." Baltimore: *Quarterly Review of Biology,* Volume 6, December, 1931.

Popenoe, Paul, *Problems of Human Reproduction.* Baltimore: The Williams & Wilkins Co., 1926.

Talmey, Bernard S., *Love.* New York: Practitioners Publishing Co., 1919.

Thomson, J. A. and Geddes, P., *Sex.* Home University Library. New York: Henry Holt & Co., 1925.

Westermarck, Edward, *The History of Human Marriage* (3 volumes). New York: The Macmillan Co., 1925.

Wright, Helena B., *The Story of Sex*. New York: The Vanguard Press, 1932.

Zuckerman, S., *The Social Life of Monkeys and Apes*. New York: Harcourt, Brace & Co., 1932.

## REFERENCES FOR ARTICLE BY ERNEST R. GROVES

Davis, Katherine Bement, *Factors in the Sex Life of 2200 Women*. New York: Harper & Brothers, 1921. Chaps. V. and VI.

Dickinson, Robert Latou, and Beam, Laura, *The Single Woman*. Baltimore: Williams and Wilkins Co., 1934.

Ellis, Havelock, *Little Essays of Love and Virtue*. London: A. & C. Black, Ltd., 1922. Chap. II.

Groves, E. R., *Marriage*. New York: Henry Holt & Co., 1933. Chap XXXI.

Knopf, O., *The Art of Being A Woman*. Boston: Little Brown & Co., 1932. Part II. Chap. III.

Taylor, W. S., A "Critique of Sublimation in Males." Worcester: *Genetic Psychology Monographs*, Vol. 13, No. 1, January, 1933.

## REFERENCES FOR ARTICLE BY ROBERT L. DICKINSON

Davis, Katharine Bement, *Factors in the Sex Life of 2200 Women*. New York: Harper and Brothers, 1929.

Dickinson, Robert Latou, *Human Sex Anatomy*. Baltimore: The Williams and Wilkins Co., 1933.

Dickinson, Robert Latou, and Beam, Laura, *A Thousand Marriages*. Baltimore: The Williams and Wilkins Co., 1931.

Dickinson, Robert Latou, and Bryant, Louise Stevens, *Control of Conception*. Baltimore: The Williams and Wilkins Co., 1934.

Dickinson, Robert Latou, and Beam, Laura, *The Single Woman*. Baltimore: The Williams and Wilkins Co., 1934.

Ellis, Havelock, *Psychology of Sex: A Manual for Students*. New York: Ray Long and Richard R. Smith, Inc., 1933.

Hamilton, G. V., *A Research in Marriage*. New York: A. & C. Boni, 1929.

Malamud, W., and Palmer, G., "The Rôle Played by Masturbation in the Causation of Mental Disturbances." New York: *Journal of Mental and Nervous Diseases,* October, 1932, pp. 220.

Strakosch, F. M., "Factors in the Sex Life of 700 Psychopathic Women." Thesis for degree of Ph.D., Columbia University, 1934.

## REFERENCES FOR ARTICLE BY ERNEST W. BURGESS

Anderson, Nels, *The Hobo, the Sociology of the Homeless Man.* Chicago: University of Chicago Press, 1923.

Blumenthal, Albert, *Small Town Stuff.* Chicago: University of Chicago Press, 1931.

Blumer, Herbert, *Movies and Conduct.* New York: The Macmillan Co., 1933.

Blumer, Herbert, and Hauser, Philip M., *Movies, Delinquency, and Crime.* New York: The Macmillan Co., 1933.

Burgess, E. W., "The Romantic Impulse and Family Disorganization," *The Survey,* 57 (1926), pp. 290–94.

Cairns, W. B., *A History of American Literature.* The Oxford University Press, 1912.

Cressey, Paul G., *The Taxi-Dance Hall; a Sociological Study in Commercial Recreation and City Life.* Chicago: University of Chicago Press, 1932.

Davis, Katharine Bement, *Factors in the Sex Life of 2200 Women.* New York: Harper and Bros., 1921.

Dell, Floyd, *Love in Greenwich Village.* New York: George H. Doran Co., 1926.

Donovan, Frances, *The Saleslady.* Chicago: University of Chicago Press, 1929.

*The Woman Who Waits.* Boston: R. G. Badger, 1920.

Lindsey, Judge B. B., *The Revolt of Modern Youth.* New York: Boni & Liveright, 1925.

Margold, Charles W., *Sex Freedom and Social Control.* Chicago: University of Chicago Press, 1926.

Park, Robert E., *The City.* Chicago: University of Chicago Press, 1925.

Park, Robert E., and Miller, H. A., *Old World Traits Transplanted.* New York: Harper and Bros., 1921.

Plant, James F., "Individual Implications of a Family Pattern," *The Family,* 11 (1930), pp. 128–32. (Evidence from a psychiatric clinic of the persistence of the family pattern.)

*Recent Social Trends in the United States.* New York: The McGraw Hill Co., 1933.

Reckless, Walter C., *Vice in Chicago.* Chicago: University of Chicago Press, 1933.

Report of the Committee on the Influence of Home Activities upon Child Education of the White House Conference. Chapter on "Sex Education." (In press, Appleton-Century Co., New York: 1934.)

Sapir, Edward, "The Discipline of Sex." New York: *American Mercury,* 16 (1929), pp. 413–30.

Sumner, W. G., *Folkways.* A Study of the Sociological Importance of Usages, Manners, Customs, Mores and Morals. Boston: Ginn & Co., 1906.

Thomas, W. I., *The Unadjusted Girl.* Boston: Little Brown & Co., 1923.

Thomas, W. I., and Znaniecki, F., *The Polish Peasant in Europe and America.* Boston: R. G. Badger, 1918–20.

Van Waters, Miriam, *Youth in Conflict.* New York: *The New Republic,* 1925.

Wood, Charles W., "The Revolution and the Individual," *The Annals of the American Academy of Political and Social Sciences,* 149 (1930), pp. 120–27.

Zorbaugh, H. W., *The Gold Coast and the Slum.* Chicago: University of Chicago Press, 1929.

## REFERENCES FOR ARTICLE BY MARY A. BEARD

Abbott, Edith, *Women in Industry.* New York: D. Appleton & Co., 1915.

Asakawa, K. I., *Some Aspects of Japanese Feudal Institutions.* New Haven: Yale University Press, 1918.

Beard, Mary R., *On Understanding Women.* New York: Longmans, Green & Co., 1931.

Branch, Mary Sydney, *Women and Wealth.* Chicago: University of Chicago Press, 1934.

Clark, Alice, *The Working Life of Women in the Seventeenth Century.* New York: Harcourt, Brace & Co., 1920.

Diehl, Guida, *Die Deutsche Frau und der National-Sozialismus.* Berlin: Neuland Verlag, 1933.

Dill, Samuel, *Roman Society from Nero to Marcus Aurelius; Roman*

*Society in the Last Century of the Western Empire; and Roman Society in Gaul in the Merovingian Age.* New York: The Macmillan Co., 1926.

Eckenstein, Lina, *Woman under Monasticism.* London: Cambridge University Press, 1896.

Kletler, Paul. *Nordwesteuropas Verkehr, Handel und Gewerbe im fruehen Mittelalter.* Jena, 1924.

Lacroix, Paul, *Histoire de la Prostitution.* Paris, 1851.

*Military and Religious Life in the Middle Ages.* London, 1874.

Lea, H. C., *An Historical Sketch of Sacerdotal Celibacy.* Philadelphia: Lippincott, 1867.

Roehm, Ernst, *Geschichte eines Hochverraters,* 7th ed. Munich: *Eher Verlag,* 1934.

Schreiner, Olive, *Woman and Labor.* New York: Frederick A. Stokes Co., 1911.

Wright, F. A., *Feminism in Greek Literature.* New York: E. P. Dutton & Co., 1923.

## REFERENCES FOR ARTICLE BY HORACE M. KALLEN

Briffault, Robert, *The Mothers.* New York: The Macmillan Co., 1927.

Carpenter, Edward, *Love's Coming of Age.* New York: Doubleday Doran & Co., 1911; The Vanguard Press, 1927.

Castiglione, B., *Perfect Courtier.* New York: E. P. Dutton & Co., 1927.

Crawley, A. E., *The Mystic Rose.* (2 vols.) New York: Boni & Liveright, 1927.

Ellis, Havelock, *Studies in the Psychology of Sex.* (Vol. 6.) Philadelphia: F. A. Davis Co., 1901. "Sex in Relation to Society."

Freud, Sigmund, *Civilization and Its Discontents.* New York: Robert O. Ballou, 1930.

Gilman, Charlotte P., *Women in Economics.* Boston: Small, Maynard & Co, 1907.

Hale, Fannina, *Woman in Soviet Russia.* New York: The Viking Press, 1934.

Hamilton, G. V., *A Research in Marriage.* New York: A. & C. Boni, 1929.

*What is Wrong with Marriage?* (with Kenneth Macgowan). New York: A. & C. Boni, 1929.

Holt, Edwin B., *The Freudian Wish*. New York: Henry Holt & Co., 1915.

Lea, Henry C., *An Historical Sketch of Sacerdotal Celibacy in the Christian Church* (2nd edition). Boston: Houghton Mifflin & Co., 1884.

Lecky, W. E. H., *History of European Morals*. New York: Appleton & Co., 1829.

Lindsey, Ben. B., *The Revolt of Modern Youth*. New York: Boni & Liveright, 1925.

*Companionate Marriage*. New York: Boni & Liveright, 1927.

Mead, Margaret, *Coming of Age in Samoa*. New York: William Morrow & Co., 1928.

*Growing Up in New Guinea*. New York: William Morrow & Co., 1930.

Plato, *The Republic*.

Pruette, Lorine, *Women and Leisure*. New York: E. P. Dutton & Co., 1924.

Russell, Bertrand, *The Conquest of Happiness*. New York: Horace Liveright, Inc., 1930.

*Marriage and Morals*. New York: Horace Liveright, Inc., 1929.

*Education and the Good Life*. New York: Boni & Liveright, 1926.

Russell, Dora, *The Right to Be Happy*. New York: Harper & Brothers, 1927.

Veblen, Thorstein, *The Instinct of Workmanship*. New York: The Viking Press, 1918.

## REFERENCES FOR ARTICLE BY LORINE PRUETTE

Davis, Katharine Bement, *Factors in The Sex Life of 2200 Women*. New York: Harper & Bros., 1929.

Dickinson, Robert Latou, and Beam, Laura, *The Single Woman: A Medical Study in Sex Education*. Baltimore: The Williams and Wilkins Co., 1934.

Pruette, Lorine, "The Flapper", in *The New Generation*. Edited by V. F. Calverton and S. B. Schmalhausen. New York: The Macaulay Co., 1930.

Pruette, Lorine, "The Revolt of the Virgins" in *Our Neurotic Age*. Edited by S. B. Schmalhausen. New York: Farrar and Rinehart, 1932.

Thomas, W. I., *The Unadjusted Girl.* Boston: Little, Brown & Co., 1923.

Thomson, J. A., and Geddes, P., *Problems of Sex.* London: Cassell and Co.

## REFERENCES FOR ARTICLE BY ROBERT MORSS LOVETT

Beach, Joseph, *The Twentieth Century Novel.* New York: Appleton-Century Co., 1932.

Lovett, R. M., and Hughes, Helen, *History of the Novel in England.* Boston: Houghton Mifflin Co., 1932.

Myer, W. L., *The New Realism.*

# REFERENCES FOR ARTICLE BY MORRIS L. ERNST

| NAME OF BOOK | CITATION | DATE | RESULT |
| --- | --- | --- | --- |
| *What Happens,* John Herrman | U. S. District Court | October 4, 1927 | Verdict for Government |
| *The Well of Loneliness,* Radclyffe Hall | City Magistrate's Court, 7th Dist. Manhattan | | Held for Special Sessions |
| *The Well of Loneliness,* Radclyffe Hall | Special Sessions, N. Y. C. | April 19, 1929 | Dismissed |
| *Birth Control Case,* | City Magistrate's Court, 2nd Dist. Manhattan | | Dismissed |
| *The Sex Side of Life,* Mary Ware Dennett | 39 Fed. (2d) 564 U. S. Circuit Court of Appeals —2nd Circuit | March 4, 1930 | Judgment reversed |
| *Casanova's Homecoming,* Arthur Schnitzler | Magistrate's Court, 4th Dist. Manhattan | September 25, 1930 | Dismissed |
| *Reigen* or *Hands Around,* Arthur Schnitzler | Magistrate's Court, 2nd Dist. Manhattan | November 27, 1929 | Dismissed |
| *Reigen* or *Hands Around,* Arthur Schnitzler | 230 A. D. 200 Appellate Division, First Dept. Manhattan | June, 1930 | Judgment of conviction affirmed—3 to 2 vote |
| *Reigen* or *Hands Around,* Arthur Schnitzler | 254 N. Y. 373 Court of Appeals, N. Y. | October 24, 1930 | Judgment affirmed—2 dissents |
| *Married Love,* Dr. Marie C. Stopes | Court of Special Sessions | 1921 | Conviction and fine |

| NAME OF BOOK | CITATION | DATE | RESULT |
|---|---|---|---|
| *Married Love,* Dr. Marie C. Stopes | 202 App. Div. 836 | July 17, 1922 | Conviction confirmed |
| *Married Love,* Dr. Marie C. Stopes | 237 N. Y. 567 | January 18, 1924 | Conviction affirmed |
| *Married Love,* Dr. Marie C. Stopes | 48 Fed. (2d) 821 U. S. District Court | April 6, 1931 | Dismissed |
| *Eastern Shame Girl,* (Anon.) *Celestine,* Octave Mirbeau | Magistrate's Court, 2nd Dist. Manhattan | May 7, 1931 | Dismissed |
| *Pay Day,* Nathan Asch | Magistrate's Court, 4th Dist. Manhattan | May 15, 1930 | Dismissed |
| *Pay Day,* Nathan Asch | General Sessions, N. Y. County | About January, 1934 | Dismissed |
| *The Sex Side of Life,* Mary Ware Dennett | U. S. District Court, Eastern Dist. of N. Y. | April 23, 1929 | Convicted, $300 fine |
| *Contraception,* Marie C. Stopes | 51 Fed. (2d) 525 U. S. District Court, Southern District of N. Y. | July 16, 1931 | Dismissed |
| *From a Turkish Harim, Hsi Men Ching,* Anonymous | City Magistrate's Court, 7th Dist. Manhattan | November 9, 1931 | Dismissed |
| ***Flesh,*** **Clement Wood** | Magistrate's Court, 2nd Dist. Manhattan | December 18, 1931 | Dismissed |

| | | | |
|---|---|---|---|
| *Female*, Donald Henderson Clarke | Magistrate's Court, 2nd Dist. Manhattan | June 7, 1933 | Dismissed |
| *Female*, Donald Henderson Clarke | Magistrate's Court, 1st Dist. Queens | April 28, 1933 | Held for Special Sessions |
| *Female*, Donald Henderson Clarke | Court of Special Sessions, Queens | August 24, 1933 | Convicted, $100 fine. Appeal pending |
| *Female*, Donald Henderson Clarke | Appellate Division, Second Department | June 22, 1934 | Unanimously affirmed |
| *Ulysses*, James Joyce | United States Dist. Court | December 6, 1933 | Libel dismissed |
| *Ulysses*, James Joyce | Circuit Court of Appeals, Second Circuit | August 7, 1934 | Dismissal upheld |

**Youngs, etc. v. Lee, etc., 45 Fed. (2d) 103 (July 21, 193?).** This case involved the sending of condoms through the mails. The Circuit Court of Appeals held that under certain circumstances they *could* be legally distributed through the mails.

People v. Wendling, 258 N. Y. 451 (March 3, 1932). This case arose out of the stage production of *Frankie and Jonnnie*. Convictions were had in the Court of Special Sessions in New York City, and were upheld by the Appellate Division. The Court of Appeals reversed the convictions and gave the play a clean bill of health.

In 1933, Sumner proceeded against Erskine Caldwell's *God's Little Acre,* in the Magistrate's Court in New York City. On June 26, 1933, Magistrate Greenspan dismissed the complaint.